# THE
# KIDS,
# FOOD and
# DIABETES
# FAMILY COOKBOOK

## GLORIA LORING

**Publisher:** Gloria Loring for the
Juvenile Diabetes Foundation International
14755 Ventura Blvd. Suite 1-744
Sherman Oaks, CA 91403

Cover Design: Judy Garcia and Carol Morris
Cover Artwork: Taryn Benarroch

This book is dedicated to my son, Brennan.

# Table of Contents

**Foreword**  vii

**Introduction to Recipes**  1

**Breakfast**  7

**Lunch**  53

**Snacks**  87

**Dinner**  125

**Master List of Recipes**  237

# Foreword

The recipes in this book were first published by Contemporary Books in 1986 as *Kids, Food & Diabetes.* The book contained advice about good nutrition, the practical aspects of being a parent of a diabetic child, and nearly 200 recipes. In the fall of 1989, I was informed that the book would no longer be available; it had been taken out of print.

I had received so many letters from parents telling me how much the book had helped them learn to live with diabetes. I knew how each of them felt: the sadness, confusion, and anger that accompanied knowing that their child had diabetes. To think that the book would no longer be available to help them made me feel, to use my mother's word, "heartsick."

I became determined to find a way to get the book republished. I called Contemporary Books and asked for the rights to the book to be returned to me. They agreed. A few weeks later, I was telling my story to an acquaintance. He put me in touch with a friend of his who is an editor for a publishing company and, within a month, I began writing an updated, expanded version of the practical advice section of *Kids, Food & Diabetes,* sans recipes. While writing the new book, *Parenting a Diabetic Child,* I kept getting requests for the previous book from parents who had heard that it contained recipes that were not only enjoyed by children with diabetes, but the rest of the family as well. As I was completing the new book, I decided to publish the recipes in a companion cookbook to raise money for diabetes research.

# Foreword

During this time, I met the CEO of the Thompson Medical Foundation, S. Daniel Abraham, a dynamic man with a passionate interest in health and good nutrition. He expressed a desire to assist the work of the Juvenile Diabetes Foundation International at some time in the future. I called and suggested that perhaps that time had come. I explained that the new cookbook would benefit JDF and he agreed to underwrite the cost of printing.

Since these recipes were first published, there have been adjustments in the food exchanges involving a difference of 10 to 20 calories, a very small amount. If you have any questions, ask your dietitian. In addition, you will come across references to material that supposedly appears before or after the recipes. Keep in mind that this recipe section was lifted from the middle of the previous book. It would have cost a lot of money to change those few references, so I chose to leave them as is. Please just overlook them.

There are many people to thank for their direct or indirect contributions to this project:

Ted Mason, for introducing me to my editor, Janice Gallagher, which was the start of both books.

Derek Gallagher, for patiently advising us and helping coordinate all the technical elements.

Arthur Barzilay, for a cigarette boat cruise that turned into fundraising support.

Judy Garcia and Carol Morris, two wonderful, creative friends who designed the cover and did the long hours of necessary work.

My friends at JDF, especially Karen Brownlee and Gloria Pennington, for their inspiration and loving support.

My niece, Taryn, for the lovely artwork that graces the cover.

Danny Abraham and the people of Ultra Slim•Fast, who have made this project possible.

Christopher, my husband, and Brennan and Robin, my sons, for their love and understanding.

Gloria Loring

# Introduction to Recipes

The recipes in this section are designed to suit the diets of diabetic children, but they're also intended to appeal to your whole family's taste buds. Every parent and health professional I interviewed felt the whole family should eat the same basic meals as the diabetic child. The psychological support of eating the same foods greatly reduced the stress of "being different." Of course, an even better reason is that it's a very healthy way to eat. These recipes make it possible for you to nourish your diabetic child *and* the rest of your family. They reflect the principles of good nutrition already outlined. They are low in fat, sugar, and salt, and many are good sources of fiber. At the same time, they're high in flavor and eye appeal.

To make planning for your diabetic child as easy as possible, this section is organized by meals: breakfast, lunch, snacks, and dinner. I've found it saves time to be able to locate a number of appropriate choices for each meal in one spot. After Brennan was diagnosed as having diabetes, I started a loose-leaf notebook along the same lines, with individual sections for breakfast, lunch, snacks, and dinner, each containing menu ideas and some recipes. Each menu was based on Brennan's allowed exchanges. Of course, your own child will have his own diet plan, so this book can't provide precise menus for everyone, but it does offer a great variety of foods and recipes and some possible combinations of recipes to give you menu ideas.

At the beginning of each meal chapter are some general guidelines for concocting nutritious menus as well as specific tips on various foods or dishes commonly served

1

at that meal and where they fit into the scheme of things for the diabetic. Your child's diabetes probably means that certain items will have to be cut from your shopping list, but I mention substitutes and alternatives wherever possible. The idea is to assist your child in learning about good nutrition and good diabetes management while making the restrictions imposed as painless as possible.

It's equally important that the job of planning and preparing your child's meals be trouble-free. Therefore, in the introductory pages of each chapter I've provided a full list of the recipes that follow, complete with their exchanges. Use it as an at-a-glance reference for designing your daily meals.

Please don't be limited by the way I've organized the recipes. Your child can certainly have leftover Spinach Manicotti for breakfast or a bowl of cereal for dinner. One of the problems with diabetes is that your child can't skip meals, no matter how much she dislikes what's on her plate. If you have a picky eater, you quickly learn the meaning of flexibility. Be as creative as you need to be in providing a finicky eater with healthy choices for meals and snacks. Toddlers can be especially difficult but will often respond to decorated foods or frozen treats like frozen bananas, frozen grapes, or homemade juice Popsicles.

At the end of the book, before the index, I've listed all the recipes by type—main dishes, desserts, vegetables, beverages, etc. This master list is meant to serve as an additional time-saver. Use it to formulate meals that correspond to your child's tastes and diet plan and that please and nourish your whole family.

Regarding servings, the best way to become familiar with the recommended portion for any exchange is to know what it looks like. For example, measure ½ cup of several different vegetables and see how much room is taken up on your child's plate. Compare a 3-ounce serving of meat, chicken, or fish to the size of your child's palm so she can see how big it is. For a week or two, weigh and measure everything and you and your child will get to a point where you can easily "eyeball" a serving and tell if it is about right. No one really expects you and your child to drag measuring cups and spoons and a scale around for the rest of your lives. Diabetes management is not a precise science. Food, exercise, and insulin requirements are a little different each day. The best we can hope for is a responsible approach and a fairly conscientious use of the tools we are given to help control blood sugar. Don't make yourself or your child crazy over one tablespoon more or less or ¼ FRUIT exchange; it's the overall picture that matters.

# A NOTE ON SWEETNESS

Some of the recipes in this book do contain a small amount of sugar. The largest amount per serving is 1 teaspoon. There's nothing inherently wrong with a small amount of sugar when it's ingested with an otherwise wholesome food that contains fiber and some protein or fat. It's the concentrated sugars served in a food with no nutritional value that are detrimental to people with diabetes. Your child's blood sugar response to food is individualized; what raises one child's sugar greatly may not affect another child nearly as much. You and your child can judge by experience which foods are no-nos. If you have any questions, consult your doctor or dietician. Something like Wholesome Brownies (see index) may be fine for your child to have before a period of exercise when the NPH insulin is also peaking, but it may not be appropriate at other times. Timing of insulin and food intake can be important, and this subject is discussed in greater depth in Part III: "The Copebook."

Concerning artificial sweeteners, I have noted when it is appropriate to use Equal (aspartame). It is preferred because, thus far, it has been shown to be safe for human consumption and approved by the FDA. Its drawback is that it breaks down at the boiling point (212°F), so it cannot be used for baking. Saccharin (Sweet'n Low and SugarTwin), on the other hand, can be heated above the boiling point but has been identified as possibly carcinogenic.

Equal, Sweet'n Low, and SugarTwin come in standardized packets of approximately 1 gram by weight that are each equal in sweetness to 2 teaspoons of sugar. This is the size packet referred to in the recipes. Six of these packets would be equal in sweetness to ¼ cup sugar. If you like to buy SugarTwin in the pour-spout box, measure it just like sugar. I have given the comparative "sugar" sweetness of the artificial sweetener in each recipe. You can use that "sugar" amount as a guide when using SugarTwin.

As a parent, you need to make a decision as to how much artificial sweetener your child ingests each day. There is the previously discussed trade-off of good control and lessened risks of complications for the use of artificial foods with unknown long-term consequences. It is best for your child to eat whole, natural foods as much as possible, but your child is going to want to have some "sweets and treats" now and then. Your doctor and dietician or nurse-educator can help you with any specific questions that arise on this issue.

# A NOTE ON INGREDIENTS

- All the fruits and juices used in these recipes are unsweetened. They can be fresh or canned in juice or water-packed. Remember that fruit juice contains carbohydrates and cannot be considered a free food for diabetics, so drain all canned fruits unless the recipe instructs otherwise.
- The baking powder used in the recipes should be double-acting. If you wish, you can get low-sodium baking powder in health food stores and double the amount listed to get the same effect.
- Zest, be it orange or lemon, refers to the colored portion of rind and does not include the white part underneath, which can be bitter.
- All the yogurt used in the recipes is plain, nonfat

yogurt. The buttermilk used should be made from skim milk. If you can't get it, get buttermilk made from low-fat milk and add 5 grams fat and 1 FAT exchange per cup used.

- All the herbs used should be dried leaves unless a recipe specifically states *ground* or *fresh*. Be sure to crush leaves in the palm of your hand or with a mortar and pestle to release the flavor before adding.
- Be sure to use fresh lemon juice. Reconstituted lemon and lime juices contain preservatives and just don't taste the same as fresh. The quality of ingredients is just as important as the recipe.
- *Don't* use garlic powder or garlic salt. Use fresh garlic. It's a wonder. Not only does it add distinctive flavor; it also is available year-round. More importantly, it possesses healthful properties far beyond just chasing vampires away. It can, in the right circumstances, lower serum cholesterol levels and triglyceride levels. Garlic and onions also contain substances that inhibit the clumping of blood cells. Clumping is the start of blood clots, which are a major factor in heart attacks and strokes.

  Choose heads of garlic that are plump, firm, dry, and free of soft or shriveled cloves. Store in a cool, dark, dry, well-ventilated spot, but not in the refrigerator, where it might sprout. Use lemon juice or salt to rid your hands or utensils of garlic odor. The chlorophyll in parsley helps freshen garlic breath.

This section was prepared under the expert guidance of Patty McCarthy and Tina Leeser. Patty, the mother of three hungry teenagers, is a gourmet chef who has studied in France. She and her mother have taught cooking classes for years in the southern California area under the name of "Cookworks." Tina closely supervised and guided the choice of recipes and provided all the nutrition and exchange information.

# Breakfast

We've all heard that a good nutritious breakfast is important; for anyone with diabetes, it's essential. Of course, every meal is essential, but breakfast can present a special problem. Your child may not feel hungry first thing in the morning. He may simply refuse to eat his complete allotment of exchanges before leaving for school. You may have to resort to sending him off with some food in hand in the hope it will be eaten on the way to school. Your child may fail to do so, as happened when I tried this with Brennan. About halfway through the morning, I got a call from school. Brennan had had a severe insulin reaction and had to be carried to the school nurse. It helped him understand why breakfast was a good idea.

What is a good breakfast? Most of us with a diabetic person in the family have a pretty good idea. We've probably been told to include BREAD, FRUIT, and MILK exchanges and maybe a MEAT exchange or two. This meal is a perfect opportunity to fill your child with high-fiber, nourishing plant protein and fiber-filled fruit. Choosing whole grains and fresh fruits with low-fat milk products is the best approach.

Don't be limited by the standard breakfast fare of cereal with milk and fruit. My boys long ago got tired of cereal every morning. That's why I've included lots of muffin recipes along with recipes for sweet potato pie and bread pudding. Actually, you can serve anything that fits your child's diet plan for breakfast. The shakes included can be presented to a finicky eater as a special treat. You can also try many of the recipes in "Snacks," such as Baked

Custard, Brennan's Rice Pudding, and Apple Crunch. Maybe you'll find a few new favorites for your child, and you can alternate them with more traditional breakfast foods. If your child likes a food, and it's nutritious, serve it.

Think about breakfast the night before, even the weekend before. On Sunday night, make a batch of muffins and a big bowl of fresh fruit salad that will provide a few breakfasts and snacks. I often bake two sweet potato pies. One is used for dinner as a side dish, and one is for breakfast and snacks the next day. Homemade bread, baked the night before, can be a welcome treat the next morning.

As I've already stressed, it's the quality of food that is so important. Here are some guidelines that will help you make the best choices for breakfast.

- Choose skim (nonfat) or low-fat milk, yogurt, and buttermilk instead of whole milk and whole milk products.
- Serve whole, fresh, seasonal fruits as much as possible. Chunks of melon or orange wedges already on the breakfast table are usually eaten without much fuss. One piece of whole fruit usually will fill you up, but it's easy to drink the equivalent of several pieces of fruit as juice without realizing it.
- Get rid of bacon. It is high in fat and salt and has added sugar. It adds nothing to your family's health. Bacon and some other preserved meats are processed with sodium nitrate and sodium nitrite, which have been found in studies to be carcinogenic. Nitrates combine with the amines in the meat protein in your stomach to form nitrosamines. Nitrosamines have caused cancer in every animal species tested. Bacon is simply not worth it. If your family is used to it or some other form of meat in the morning, try home-made sausage or a plain hamburger patty instead (with wheat germ added for extra nutrition). If you must use it occasionally, use Canadian bacon or

pancetta, an Italian bacon available in Italian delis. Pancetta is cured with salt but without nitrates.

- Carbohydrates, ideally complex ones, are an important part of your breakfast menu. Remember, as a rule, the more processed a food, the less complex and more refined the carbohydrates. Refined carbohydrates generally cause the blood sugar to rise more quickly and to higher levels than complex ones containing more fiber. Also, the less refining, the more naturally occurring nutrients that will be present.
- A small amount of fat at each meal (1 FAT exchange or 1 teaspoon) helps delay the rise of blood sugar. This fat may be in muffins or pancakes or may be the margarine used on toast.
- Stay away from commercial granola and "natural" cereals. They have too much added fat and sugar. The sugar takes many forms—honey, brown sugar, corn syrup, and molasses. The fat is usually saturated vegetable fat, such as coconut or palm oil or hydrogenated soybean oil. Granola has less fiber than you would think, often less than Grape Nuts.

Be very careful about how you select the cereals you buy. As a general rule, the shorter the list of ingredients, the more nutritious the product. Look for a whole grain as the first listed ingredient, preferably with no added sugar or salt. Some good choices are:

> Nabisco's Spoon Size Shredded Wheat
> Oat Bran
> Wheatena
> Farina or Cream of Wheat
> Nutri-Grain, Wheat or Corn
> Wheaties
> Wheat Chex
> Total
> Puffed Wheat
> Quaker Oats—old-fashioned or quick-cooking

(don't use the instant; it's high in sodium
and sugar and has many additives)
Fortified Oat Flakes
Grape Nuts

Ingredients are listed on packages by order of weight. In other words, there's more of the first ingredient than anything else. Obviously, you won't buy a cereal that has sugar as the first ingredient. Check the "Carbohydrate Information" on the side of the box. Look for products that contain no more than 3 or 4 grams sucrose and other sugars (1 teaspoon of sugar weighs about 4 grams). Cereals with raisins or dates would show a higher sugar content, but it is provided by the fruit, which is high in nutrients and not just empty calories.

Most recommended serving portions of cereals appropriate for your diabetic are counted as 1½–2 BREAD exchanges, according to *The Diabetic's Brand-Name Food Exchange Handbook* by Andrea Barrett (Running Press, Philadelphia, 1984). That includes cereals with and without raisins and dates. Granola is higher in calories and counted as 1–1½ BREAD and ½–1½ FRUIT exchanges.

Also watch for sodium levels in cereals, as they can be very high. Reasonable amounts of sodium, less than 200 grams, are found in Nutri-Grain, All Bran, Most, Product 19, and Grape Nuts. Many hot cereals have less than 10 milligrams of sodium per serving, but adding only ⅛ teaspoon of salt per serving adds 275 milligrams. Try adding ⅛ teaspoon of cinnamon and a little artificial sweetener or a few chopped dates or raisins per serving instead of salt.

# BREAKFAST MENU IDEAS

These will need to be altered to fit your child's diet plan, but they should give you some ideas. If you use low-fat (2-percent) milk versus skim milk, add 1 FAT per cup. If you use low-fat yogurt versus nonfat yogurt, add 1 FAT per cup. (Check the index to locate recipes.)

## MENU 1

Strawberry Shake            ⅔ FRUIT, 1 MILK, ½ FAT
Cinnamon Toast              1 BREAD, 1 FAT

**TOTAL:** 1 BREAD, ⅔ FRUIT, 1 MILK, 1½ FAT

## MENU 2

Apple Spice Oatmeal         1½ BREAD, ½ FRUIT
8 ounces skim milk          1 MILK
½ orange, cut into wedges   ½ FRUIT

**TOTAL:** 1½ BREAD, 1 FRUIT, 1 MILK

## MENU 3

2 Orange Cottage Cheese     2 BREAD, 1 FAT
   Muffins
.8 ounces skim milk         1 MILK
½ banana or 1 small apple   1 FRUIT

**TOTAL:** 2 BREAD, 1 FRUIT, 1 MILK, 1 FAT

## MENU 4

½ cup Bread Pudding         1 BREAD, ½ MILK, 1 FAT
1 orange, cut into wedges   1 FRUIT
4 ounces skim milk          ½ MILK

**TOTAL:** 1 BREAD, 1 FRUIT, 1 MILK, 1 FAT

## MENU 5

1 wedge Robin's Favorite:   1½ BREAD, 1 FRUIT, ½ lean
   Sweet Potato Pie            MEAT, 1 FAT
8 ounces skim milk          1 MILK

**TOTAL:** 1½ BREAD, 1 FRUIT, 1 MILK, ½ lean MEAT, 1 FAT

## MENU 6

2 Multigrain Pancakes       1½ BREAD, 1 FAT
½ cup Blueberry Sauce       1 FRUIT
8 ounces skim milk          1 MILK

**TOTAL:** 1½ BREAD, 1 FRUIT, 1 MILK, 1 FAT

## MENU 7

| | |
|---|---|
| 1 cup Ambrosia | 1½ FRUIT, trace FAT |
| 1 Homemade Sausage patty | 1½ lean MEAT |
| 1 Blueberry Muffin | 1 BREAD, ½ FAT |
| 8 ounces skim milk | 1 MILK |

**TOTAL:** 1 BREAD, 1½ FRUIT, 1 MILK, 1½ lean MEAT, ½ FAT

# BREAKFAST EXCHANGES
# (Per Serving)

Use this list as a quick reference when planning breakfast menus. A glance at the right-hand column should give you ideas of what to serve for certain exchanges called for in your child's diet plan. The recipes are listed here in the same order as they appear in the chapter.

| | |
|---|---|
| Banana Shake | ½ BREAD, 1 FRUIT, 1 MILK |
| Orange-Pineapple Shake | 2 FRUIT, ⅓ MILK |
| Strawberry Shake | ⅔ FRUIT, 1 MILK, ½ FAT |
| Homemade Cocoa Mix | ½ MILK, ½ FAT |
| Berry Yogurt | ½ FRUIT, ½ MILK, ½ FAT |
| Peach Yogurt | ½ FRUIT, ½ MILK, ½ FAT |
| Ambrosia | 1½ FRUIT, trace FAT |
| Spiced Baked Apples | 2 FRUIT |
| Apple Spice Oatmeal | 1½ BREAD, ½ FRUIT |
| Stovetop Granola | 1 BREAD, 1 FAT |
| Homemade Sausage | 1½ lean MEAT |
| Eggs Benedict | 1 BREAD, 2 medium-fat MEAT |
| Mock Hollandaise Sauce | ½ medium-fat MEAT |
| Bread Pudding | 1 BREAD, ½ MILK, 1 FAT |
| Robin's Favorite: Sweet Potato Pie | 1½ BREAD, 1 FRUIT, ½ lean MEAT, 1 FAT |
| Raisin Cheese Toast | 1 BREAD, 1 medium-fat MEAT |
| Variation 3 | 1 BREAD, 1 FRUIT, 1 medium-fat MEAT |

| | |
|---|---|
| Cinnamon Toast | 1 BREAD, 1 FAT |
| French Toast | 1 BREAD, 1½ lean MEAT |
| Baked Apple Pancake | 1 BREAD, 1 FRUIT, 1 medium-fat MEAT |
| Multigrain Pancakes | 1½ BREAD, 1 FAT |
| Cheese Blintzes | 1 BREAD, 2 medium-fat MEAT |
| Bran Crêpes | 1 BREAD, 2 medium-fat MEAT |
| Strawberry Sauce | 1 FRUIT/Less than ⅔ cup FREE |
| Mock Sour Cream | ⅓ lean MEAT |
| Gloria's Corn Bread | 1 BREAD, 1 FAT |
| Buttermilk Biscuits | ⅔ BREAD, ½ FAT |
| Banana Bread | 1 BREAD, 1 FRUIT, ½ FAT |
| High-Protein Three-Grain Bread | 1½ BREAD |
| Whole Grain Irish Soda Bread | 1½ BREAD, 1 FAT |
| Refrigerator Bran Muffins | 1 BREAD, ½ FRUIT, 1 FAT |
| Applesauce Muffins | 1 BREAD, 1 FRUIT, ½ FAT |
| Blueberry Muffins | 1 BREAD, ½ FAT |
| Orange Cottage Cheese Muffins | 1 BREAD, ½ FAT |
| Oat Bran Muffins | 1 BREAD, ½ lean MEAT, 1 FAT |
| Lemon Muffins | 1 BREAD, 1 FAT |
| Strawberry Jam | Up to ¼ cup FREE |
| Blueberry Jam Spread | Up to ¼ cup FREE |
| Microwave Peach Jam | Up to ½ cup FREE |
| Fresh Blueberry Sauce | Up to ¼ cup FREE |
| Applesauce | 1¼ FRUIT |

# Recipes

## BREAKFAST SHAKES AND BEVERAGES

When accompanied by a piece of high-protein toast, breakfast shakes are one of the quickest breakfasts to prepare. Shakes like this are appealing to many children because they remind them of ice cream shakes. They also break the monotony of a glass of milk and a piece of fruit. See also "Snacks" for other breakfast shake possibilities.

## Banana Shake

½  banana, peeled
1  cup skim milk *or* ¾ cup skim milk and ¼ cup plain low-fat yogurt
2  tablespoons wheat germ
1  teaspoon vanilla extract

**1.** Put ½ banana in freezer the night before you plan to serve the shake.
**2.** Put all ingredients in a blender or food processor, blend until smooth, and serve.

*Yield: 1 1¼-cup serving*

| Nutritive values per serving: | CAL | CHO (gm) | PRO (gm) | FAT (gm) |
|---|---|---|---|---|
| | 155 | 28 | 9 | 0 |

Food exchanges per serving:    ½ BREAD, 1 FRUIT, 1 MILK

# Orange-Pineapple Shake

½ cup unsweetened orange juice
½ cup crushed pineapple, in juice
2 tablespoons instant nonfat dry milk
¼ teaspoon vanilla extract

Put all ingredients in a blender or food processor, blend until smooth, and serve.

*Yield: 1 1-cup serving*

| Nutritive values per serving: | CAL | CHO (gm) | PRO (gm) | FAT (gm) |
|---|---|---|---|---|
| | 107 | 24 | 3 | 0 |

Food exchanges per serving:  2 FRUIT, ⅓ MILK

# Strawberry Shake

½ cup skim milk
½ cup plain low-fat yogurt
½ cup frozen unsweetened whole strawberries
½ teaspoon vanilla extract
1 packet artificial sweetener (Equal)

Put all ingredients in a blender or food processor, blend until smooth, and serve.

*Yield: 1 1½-cup serving*

| Nutritive values per serving: | CAL | CHO (gm) | PRO (gm) | FAT (gm) |
|---|---|---|---|---|
| | 106 | 19 | 8 | 2½ |

Food exchanges per serving:  ⅔ FRUIT, 1 MILK, ½ FAT

# Homemade Cocoa Mix

*There are now several good sugar-free cocoa mixes on the market, but it is more economical to make your own with this recipe.*

¾ cup cocoa (unsweetened)
1 quart instant nonfat dry milk
16 packets artificial sweetener (Equal)

1. Mix ingredients well and store in an airtight container in a moderately cool place.
2. Use 3 tablespoons mix plus 8 ounces of boiling water for each serving.

*Yield: 24 8-ounce cups cocoa*

| Nutritive values per 8-ounce serving: | CAL | CHO (gm) | PRO (gm) | FAT (gm) |
|---|---|---|---|---|
| | 65 | 5 | 4 | 4 |

Food exchanges per 8-ounce serving:　　½ MILK, ½ FAT

# FRUITY BREAKFAST TREATS

## Berry Yogurt

½ cup blueberries, raspberries, or
   strawberries (fresh or frozen, unsweetened)
2 packets artificial sweetener (Equal)
¼ teaspoon vanilla extract
1 cup low-fat yogurt*

**1.** Wash blueberries; mash them with sweetener.
**2.** Stir vanilla into yogurt; fold in berries.
**3.** Chill in small container for several hours or overnight.

*Yield: 2 ¾-cup servings*

| Nutritive values per ¾-cup serving: | CAL | CHO (gm) | PRO (gm) | FAT (gm) |
|---|---|---|---|---|
| | 60 | 11 | 4 | 2½ |

Food exchanges per ¾-cup
serving:                    ½ FRUIT, ½ MILK, ½ FAT

---

*If you use nonfat yogurt, subtract ½ FAT.

## Peach Yogurt

⅔ cup fresh peaches, pared and diced, or
   canned peaches in juice, drained
1 teaspoon fresh lemon juice
2 packets artificial sweetener (Equal)
¼ teaspoon ground mace or nutmeg
1 cup plain low-fat yogurt*

**1.** Slightly mash diced peaches with lemon juice, sweetener, and mace or nutmeg.
**2.** Stir in yogurt; blend well.
**3.** Chill in a covered container several hours or overnight.

*Yield: 2 ¾-cup servings*

| Nutritive values per ¾-cup serving: | CAL | CHO (gm) | PRO (gm) | FAT (gm) |
|---|---|---|---|---|
| | 64 | 12 | 4 | 2½ |

Food exchanges per ¾-cup
serving:                          ½ FRUIT, ½ MILK, ½ FAT

---

*If you use nonfat yogurt, subtract ½ FAT.

# Ambrosia

*Fresh fruit salad is great for breakfast or anytime. Use
any combination of fruit you like. Unsweetened coconut
can be found at health food stores. If you can't find it, you
can use sweetened coconut. It would add a few calories
per serving but not change the exchange values.*

  2  small apples, sliced
  2  medium grapefruit, peeled and sectioned
  2  medium oranges, peeled and sectioned
  ½  cup unsweetened orange juice
  2  tablespoons shredded coconut
     (unsweetened if available)
     Mint sprigs (optional)

**1.** Combine first 4 ingredients; cover and chill 1 hour.
**2.** Arrange fruit in individual serving dishes; sprinkle
   with coconut and garnish with mint if desired.

*Yield: approximately 6 1-cup servings*

| Nutritive values per 1-cup serving: | CAL | CHO (gm) | PRO (gm) | FAT (gm) |
|---|---|---|---|---|
| | 74 | 16 | 0 | 1 |

Food exchanges per 1-cup
serving:                          1½ FRUIT, trace FAT

# Spiced Baked Apples

4   medium cooking apples
½   cup water
1   teaspoon fresh lemon juice
    Ground cinnamon, mace, and nutmeg

1. Preheat oven to 375°F.
2. Core apples to within ½ inch of bottom, leaving an inch-wide cavity. Peel about a 1-inch strip of skin from stem end of each apple.
3. Arrange apples in an 8-inch square or 9-inch round baking pan. Combine water and lemon juice; pour over apples. Sprinkle a pinch of cinnamon, mace, and nutmeg on each apple.
4. Cover and bake for 50–60 minutes, until apples are tender. Or put in microwave on HIGH for 4–6 minutes, until apples are tender, turning dish about halfway through the cooking time.

*Yield: 4 servings*

| Nutritive values per serving: | CAL | CHO (gm) | PRO (gm) | FAT (gm) |
|---|---|---|---|---|
| | 80 | 20 | 0 | 0 |
| Food exchanges per serving: | 2 FRUIT | | | |

# CEREALS

# Apple Spice Oatmeal

*This is a much healthier version of the commercial instant oatmeal. It contains much less sodium and no sugar. Oatmeal has twice the protein content of corn or wheat flakes cereal.*

> 2 cups water
> 1 cup rolled oats (regular or quick, not instant)
> $\frac{1}{8}$ teaspoon salt, if desired
> 1 apple, peeled and chopped or grated
> $\frac{1}{2}$ teaspoon ground cinnamon

**1.** In a heavy saucepan, combine the water, oats, salt, and apples. Bring to a boil, reduce heat, cover, and simmer for 5 minutes, stirring often.

**2.** Stir in cinnamon just before serving.

**Variation**

Substitute 3 dates, finely chopped, for the apple.

*Yield: 3 ¾-cup servings*

| Nutritive values per ¾-cup serving: | CAL | CHO (gm) | PRO (gm) | FAT (gm) |
|---|---|---|---|---|
| | 138 | 25 | 5 | 2 |

| Food exchanges per ¾-cup serving: | 1½ BREAD, ½ FRUIT | | | |
|---|---|---|---|---|

# Stovetop Granola

*This is much better for you than the commercial granolas. Try a ¼-cup serving sprinkled over other cereal or stirred into berry yogurt for extra flavor and nutrition. If you can't find unsweetened coconut, use sweetened.*

     1¼   cups oatmeal (old-fashioned, regular or quick, not instant)
     ⅓   cup chopped walnuts or chopped unsalted peanuts
     ¼   cup wheat germ
     ⅓   cup sesame seeds
     ⅓   cup shredded coconut (unsweetened if available)
     ¼   cup raisins
     ½   teaspoon ground cinnamon

1. Place the oatmeal and nuts in a large cast iron skillet over medium heat. Stir constantly for about 5 minutes.
2. Add the wheat germ, sesame seeds, and coconut. Stir occasionally for another 10 minutes.
3. Remove from the heat and let cool to room temperature.
4. Add the raisins and cinnamon and stir. Store in an airtight container.

*Yield: 10 ¼-cup servings*

| Nutritive values per ¼-cup serving: | CAL | CHO (gm) | PRO (gm) | FAT (gm) |
|---|---|---|---|---|
| | 111 | 11 | 4 | 7 |

| Food exchanges per ¼-cup serving: | 1 BREAD, 1 FAT |
|---|---|

# MEAT DISHES

# Homemade Sausage

1 pound very lean ground beef
1 teaspoon sage
½ teaspoon thyme
½ teaspoon salt
1 teaspoon finely ground pepper

1. Mix all ingredients together thoroughly.
2. Shape into 8 patties.
3. Broil. If pan-frying, drain off the fat as it collects.
4. Drain patties on paper towels.

*Yield: 8 patties*

| Nutritive values per 1-patty serving: | CAL | CHO (gm) | PRO (gm) | FAT (gm) |
|---|---|---|---|---|
| | 85 | 0 | 10 | 5 |

Food exchanges per 1-patty
serving:                              1½ lean MEAT

# Eggs Benedict

½ teaspoon peanut oil
6 1-ounce slices Canadian bacon
6 poached eggs
3 English muffins, split and toasted
  Mock Hollandaise Sauce (recipe follows)

1. Wipe a large skillet with oil; place over medium heat until hot. Place Canadian bacon in skillet; cook 3 minutes on each side or until browned. Place on paper towels to drain.
2. Place 1 slice Canadian bacon and 1 poached egg on each muffin half; top each with 2 tablespoons Mock Hollandaise Sauce. Serve immediately.

*Yield: 6 servings*

| Nutritive values per serving: | CAL | CHO (gm) | PRO (gm) | FAT (gm) |
|---|---|---|---|---|
| | 232 | 15 | 17 | 11 |

Food exchanges per serving:      1 BREAD, 2 medium-fat MEAT

# Mock Hollandaise Sauce

*You can use low-fat instead of nonfat yogurt; it will add only a negligible amount of fat per serving:*

        1   egg yolk
        ½   cup nonfat yogurt
        1   tablespoon fresh lemon juice
        ⅛   teaspoon freshly ground white pepper

**1.** Combine all ingredients in a small saucepan; stir with a wire whisk until smooth.
**2.** Cook mixture over low heat, stirring constantly, 3–4 minutes or until thoroughly heated. Serve warm. (The sauce can be reheated, if necessary, but *very slowly* over very low heat.)

*Yield: ¾ cup*

| Nutritive values per 2-tablespoon serving: | CAL | CHO (gm) | PRO (gm) | FAT (gm) |
|---|---|---|---|---|
| | 8 | 5 | 5 | 4 |

| Food exchanges per 2-tablespoon serving: | ½ medium-fat MEAT |
|---|---|

# PUDDING AND PIE FOR BREAKFAST
## Bread Pudding

½  teaspoon vegetable oil
4  slices whole wheat bread, cubed
¼  cup golden raisins or currants
2  whole eggs
2  egg whites
1  12-ounce can evaporated skim milk
½  cup skim milk
6  packets artificial sweetener (equal to ¼ cup sugar)
½  teaspoon ground cinnamon
2  teaspoons vanilla extract
1  teaspoon finely grated lemon or orange zest

1. Preheat oven to 325°F.
2. Wipe a 1½-quart casserole with oil. Place bread in bottom of casserole. Scatter raisins on top.
3. Beat eggs and egg whites until foamy; mix in remaining ingredients.
4. Pour egg mixture over bread.
5. Place casserole in a shallow pan. Pour hot water to depth of 1 inch around casserole.
6. Bake 1 hour, until a knife inserted halfway between center and outside edge comes out clean.

*Yield: 8 ½-cup servings*

| Nutritive values per ½-cup serving: | CAL | CHO (gm) | PRO (gm) | FAT (gm) |
|---|---|---|---|---|
| | 145 | 16 | 9 | 5 |

Food exchanges per ½-cup serving:    1 BREAD, ½ MILK, 1 FAT

# Robin's Favorite:
# Sweet Potato Pie

*Robin, my younger son, is a fussy eater. This is one dish that gets him excited about breakfast. I often make two of these, one for dinner and one for breakfast the next morning. They don't last long. I prefer to use yams because the texture is smoother than that of sweet potatoes. Instead of mixing this with a blender or food processor, use a potato masher or food mill. The fiber won't break down quite so much.*

> 1 egg white
> 2 whole eggs
> 3 medium sweet potatoes or yams, cooked and peeled
> 6 packets artificial sweetener (equal to ¼ cup sugar)
> 1 8-ounce can crushed pineapple in juice, undrained
> ¾ cup evaporated skim milk
> 1 teaspoon vanilla extract
> ¼ teaspoon each ground nutmeg, ginger, and cinnamon
> 1 unbaked 9-inch pie shell

**1.** Preheat oven to 425°F.
**2.** Beat egg white and eggs in food processor.
**3.** Mash sweet potatoes and combine with egg mixture.
**4.** Add remaining ingredients except pie shell and mix well to combine.
**5.** Pour into pie shell and bake for 10 minutes. Reduce heat to 325°F and bake another 45 minutes. A knife inserted in the center should come out relatively clean.

*Yield: 8 servings*

| Nutritive values per serving: | CAL | CHO (gm) | PRO (gm) | FAT (gm) |
|---|---|---|---|---|
| | 210 | 31 | 6 | 7 |
| Food exchanges per serving: | 1½ BREAD, 1 FRUIT, ½ lean MEAT, 1 FAT | | | |

# TOAST, PANCAKES, AND MORE

## Raisin Cheese Toast

¼ cup low-fat cottage cheese
1 packet artificial sweetener (Equal)
¼ teaspoon maple extract
   Dash ground nutmeg or cinnamon
1 slice whole wheat raisin bread, toasted

1. Combine the first 4 ingredients and spread on bread.
2. Place bread on foil or broiler pan and broil 6 inches from heat until cheese is hot and bubbly. Or use the toaster oven for the same result.

**Variations**
1. Use ½ English muffin instead of bread.
2. Substitute 2 tablespoons unsweetened orange juice and ½ teaspoon grated orange zest for maple extract and spices.
3. Omit maple extract, use ⅛ teaspoon ground cinnamon, and top with ½ banana, 1 peach, or 1 apple, sliced. Then broil as above.

*Yield: 1 serving*

| Nutritive values per serving: | CAL | CHO (gm) | PRO (gm) | FAT (gm) |
|---|---|---|---|---|
| | 150 | 19 | 7 | 5 |
| Food exchanges per serving: | 1 BREAD, 1 medium-fat MEAT | | | |

| Nutritive values of Variation 2 per serving: | CAL | CHO (gm) | PRO (gm) | FAT (gm) |
|---|---|---|---|---|
| | 160 | 19 | 7 | 5 |
| Food exchanges of Variation 2 per serving: | (exchanges unaffected) | | | |

| Nutritive values of Variation 3 per serving: | CAL | CHO (gm) | PRO (gm) | FAT (gm) |
|---|---|---|---|---|
| | 173 | 25 | 7 | 5 |

Food exchanges of Variation 3 per serving: 1 BREAD, 1 FRUIT, 1 medium-fat MEAT

# Cinnamon Toast

*Even the little ones can help make this!*

1 slice high-fiber or high-protein whole wheat bread
1 teaspoon diet margarine
Ground cinnamon
1 packet artificial sweetener (Equal)

1. Toast the bread.
2. Spread on the margarine, and sprinkle on the cinnamon and sweetener.

*Yield: 1 serving*

| Nutritive values per serving: | CAL | CHO (gm) | PRO (gm) | FAT (gm) |
|---|---|---|---|---|
| | 115 | 15 | 2 | 5 |

Food exchanges per serving: 1 BREAD, 1 FAT

# French Toast

*I like Nathan Pritikin's advice about cutting cholesterol whenever possible. Instead of using 2 whole eggs, I discard the yolk from one and cut down on the cholesterol. Try it for any egg recipe you use. Two egg whites equal one whole egg in volume.*

> 1 egg white
> 1 whole egg
> ¼ cup skim milk
> ¼ teaspoon ground cinnamon
> ⅛ teaspoon ground nutmeg
> ½ teaspoon vanilla extract
> 4 slices whole wheat bread
> ½ teaspoon peanut oil

1. In a pie plate, mix all ingredients except bread and oil. Dip bread into mixture, one slice at a time, turning to coat both sides.
2. Wipe a nonstick griddle with the oil and heat over medium heat. Cook each side until golden.

**Variation**
Substitute ⅓ cup unsweetened orange juice for the milk and 1 teaspoon grated orange zest for the cinnamon.

*Yield: 4 slices*

| Nutritive values per 1-slice serving: | CAL | CHO (gm) | PRO (gm) | FAT (gm) |
|---|---|---|---|---|
| | 102 | 16 | 6 | 1 |

| Food exchanges per 1-slice serving: | 1 BREAD, 1½ lean MEAT |
|---|---|

# Baked Apple Pancake

*This is a slight variation on a recipe from* The Art of Cooking for the Diabetic, *by Katharine Middleton and Mary Abbott Hess (Contemporary Books, 1978).*

| | |
|---|---|
| 1 | large cooking apple |
| ½ | cup skim milk |
| ½ | cup unbleached white flour |
| 2 | whole eggs, beaten |
| 1 | egg white |
| 1 | teaspoon sugar |
| ½ | teaspoon vanilla extract |
| | Dash salt |
| 2 | tablespoons diet margarine |
| 1 | teaspoon ground cinnamon |
| 4 | packets artificial sweetener (Equal) |
| 2 | tablespoons fresh lemon juice |

1. Preheat oven to 400°F.
2. Core apple and slice very thin.
3. Combine the skim milk, flour, eggs and egg white, sugar, vanilla, and salt. Mix until smooth. *Do not beat.*
4. Melt 1 tablespoon of the margarine in a 10-inch frying pan and "roll" it around so sides and bottom are covered. Add apple slices and sauté slightly.
5. Pour batter on top evenly. Bake in oven about 10 minutes or until pancake is puffy and nearly cooked. Sprinkle with cinnamon and sweetener, dot with remaining 1 tablespoon margarine, and return to oven to brown pancake.
6. Before serving, sprinkle with lemon juice. Cut in quarters to serve.

*Yield: 4 servings*

| Nutritive values per serving: | CAL | CHO (gm) | PRO (gm) | FAT (gm) |
|---|---|---|---|---|
| | 190 | 27 | 7 | 5 |

Food exchanges per serving: 1 BREAD, 1 FRUIT, 1 medium-fat MEAT

# Multigrain Pancakes

*These healthy goodies are from* Jane Brody's Good Food Book. *My kids said they were the best pancakes I ever made. Serve them with "lite" syrup or topped with sliced apples or pears sautéed in a little water in a nonstick pan with a generous sprinkling of cinnamon. (A note about "lite" syrups: they contain less sugar and can be counted as a FRUIT. For example, 2 tablespoons of Aunt Jemima Lite has 13 grams carbohydrate and would be 1⅓ FRUIT.) If you do not have oat flour or an alternative, simply add another ¼ cup of whole wheat flour to the dry-ingredients mixture.*

### Dry Ingredients

⅔ cup whole wheat flour, preferably stone-ground

⅓ cup unbleached white flour

¼ cup oat or other flour (e.g., cornmeal, barley, buckwheat, or millet flour)

2 tablespoons wheat germ

2 teaspoons sugar

1 teaspoon double-acting baking powder

½ teaspoon baking soda

### Wet Ingredients

1 cup low-fat buttermilk

¼ cup or more skim milk

1 egg white

1 whole egg

1 tablespoon vegetable oil

¼ teaspoon vanilla extract (optional)

1. Mix together all the dry ingredients in a medium bowl.
2. In a second bowl, combine all the wet ingredients, whipping them enough to beat the egg white and the whole egg lightly. Add these to the dry ingredients, stirring just to combine them. The batter can stand for 10 minutes out of the refrigerator or for an hour or more refrigerated.

**3.** Heat the griddle over medium heat. Grease it lightly (if not nonstick) and immediately pour in ¼ cup batter. Try to leave some space between the pancakes to keep them from sticking together. Turn the heat down to moderately low and cook the pancakes until the bottoms are golden brown and the tops begin to bubble. Flip them over and cook them until the undersides are golden brown. Serve them immediately.

*Yield: 12 pancakes*

| Nutritive values per 2-pancake serving: | CAL | CHO (gm) | PRO (gm) | FAT (gm) |
|---|---|---|---|---|
| | 140 | 23 | 5 | 3 |

| Food exchanges per 2-pancake serving: | 1½ BREAD, 1 FAT |
|---|---|

# Cheese Blintzes

2 12-ounce cartons low-fat cottage cheese
1 egg, beaten
4 packets artificial sweetener (Equal)
1½ teaspoons grated lemon zest
¼ teaspoon vanilla extract
16 Bran Crêpes (recipe follows)
2 recipes Strawberry Sauce (recipe follows)
Mock Sour Cream (optional) (recipe follows)

1. Preheat oven to 350°F.
2. Combine first 5 ingredients and stir well. Spoon about 3 tablespoons cheese filling in center of each blintz. Fold right and left sides over filling; then fold bottom and top over filling, forming a square.
3. Use a nonstick baking sheet. Place blintzes, seam side down, on baking sheet; bake for 12 minutes or until thoroughly heated.
4. Top each serving of 2 blintzes with ⅓ cup Strawberry Sauce. Serve with Mock Sour Cream if desired and add appropriate exchanges.

*Yield: 16 blintzes*

| Nutritive values per 2-blintz serving (with filling and sauce): | CAL | CHO (gm) | PRO (gm) | FAT (gm) |
|---|---|---|---|---|
| | 185 | 12 | 14 | 9 |

Food exchanges per 2-blintz
serving (with filling and sauce):     1 BREAD, 2 medium-fat MEAT

# Bran Crêpes

3 eggs
1½ cups skim milk
1 cup all-purpose flour
⅓ cup 100 percent bran cereal
2 packets artificial sweetener (equal to 4
  teaspoons sugar)
¼ teaspoon salt
2 teaspoons vegetable oil

1. Combine all ingredients except oil in container of a blender or food processor; process 30 seconds. Scrape down sides of blender container with a rubber spatula; process an additional 30 seconds or until smooth. Refrigerate batter 1 hour. (This allows flour particles to swell and soften so that crepes are light in texture.)
2. Wipe the bottom of a 6-inch nonstick skillet with a bit of oil; place pan over medium heat until just hot, not smoking.
3. Pour about 2 tablespoons batter into pan. Quickly tilt pan in all directions so that batter covers the pan in a thick film; cook crêpe about 1 minute.
4. Lift edge of crêpe to test for doneness. Crêpe is ready for flipping when it can be shaken loose from pan. Flip the crêpe and cook for about 30 seconds. (This side is rarely more than spotty brown and is the side on which filling is placed).
5. When crêpe is done, place on a towel to cool. Repeat procedure until all batter is used, stirring batter occasionally. Stack crêpes between layers of waxed paper to prevent sticking.

*Yield: 16 crêpes*

| Nutritive values per 2-crêpe serving: | CAL | CHO (gm) | PRO (gm) | FAT (gm) |
|---|---|---|---|---|
| | 82 | 12 | 4 | 2 |

Food exchanges per 2-crêpe
serving:                    1 BREAD, ½ FAT

# Strawberry Sauce

*This is good not only with blintzes but also with Vanilla Cheesecake (see index for recipe).*

> 1½  cups fresh whole strawberries
> 1  packet artificial sweetener (Equal)
> 1  tablespoon fresh lemon juice

**1.** Wash berries and remove hulls and bad spots. Cut berries into bite-sized pieces.
**2.** Place in a bowl, crushing bottom layer slightly with a fork. Add sweetener and lemon juice and mix well.
**3.** Cover and chill.

*Yield: 1⅓ cups*

| Nutritive values per ⅔-cup serving: | CAL | CHO (gm) | PRO (gm) | FAT (gm) |
|---|---|---|---|---|
|  | 40 | 10 | 0 | 0 |

| Food exchanges per ⅔-cup serving: | 1 FRUIT (up to ½ cup FREE) |
|---|---|

# Mock Sour Cream

*Also use this on baked potatoes.*

> ½  cup low-fat cottage cheese
> 1½  teaspoons fresh lemon juice

**1.** Combine all ingredients in container of a blender or food processor; process on medium-high speed until smooth and creamy.
**2.** Cover and chill thoroughly.

*Yield: ½ cup*

| Nutritive values per 2-tablespoon serving: | CAL | CHO (gm) | PRO (gm) | FAT (gm) |
|---|---|---|---|---|
|  | 20 | 0 | 2 | 1 |

| Food exchanges per 2-tablespoon serving: | ⅓ lean MEAT |
|---|---|

# BREADS, BISCUITS, AND MUFFINS

## Gloria's Corn Bread

*I don't make this often because I could finish the whole pan myself—not to mention the difficulty of keeping Brennan from eating too much of it! It's filled with fiber that helps slow down the rise of blood sugar. That's important to your child.*

        1 cup unbleached white flour
        1 cup stone-ground cornmeal
        ½ teaspoon salt
        2 teaspoons double-acting baking powder
        ½ cup wheat germ
        1 cup skim milk
        2 tablespoons vegetable oil
        3 packets artificial sweetener (equal to 2
            tablespoons sugar)
        1 whole egg
        2 egg whites
        1 cup fresh or frozen corn

1. Preheat oven to 400°F.
2. Combine flour, cornmeal, salt, baking powder, and wheat germ.
3. Add remaining ingredients and stir well.
4. Pour into well-greased 8- by 8-inch pan.
5. Bake 20–25 minutes.

*Yield: 16 2-inch squares*

| Nutritive values per serving: | CAL | CHO (gm) | PRO (gm) | FAT (gm) |
|---|---|---|---|---|
| | 105 | 18 | 4 | 2 |

| Food exchanges per serving: | 1 BREAD, 1 FAT |
|---|---|

# Buttermilk Biscuits

1½  cups unbleached white flour, sifted
½  cup whole wheat flour
2  teaspoons double-acting baking powder
½  teaspoon baking soda
½  teaspoon salt
1  tablespoon sugar
5  tablespoons diet margarine
¾  cup low-fat buttermilk

**1.** Preheat oven to 425°F.
**2.** Sift together dry ingredients.
**3.** Cut in margarine with a pastry blender or 2 knives.
**4.** Add buttermilk all at once; blend with a fork just until flour is moistened and dough pulls away from the side of the bowl.
**5.** Turn out onto a lightly floured board or wax paper. Knead lightly for 30 seconds.
**6.** Roll out to a thickness of ½ inch. Cut with a 2-inch round cutter. Place 1 inch apart on a baking sheet. Bake 12–15 minutes.

*Yield: 16 2½-inch biscuits*

| Nutritive values per 1-biscuit serving: | CAL | CHO (gm) | PRO (gm) | FAT (gm) |
|---|---|---|---|---|
| | 72 | 12 | 1 | 2 |

Food exchanges per 1-biscuit serving:                    ⅔ BREAD, ½ FAT

# Banana Bread

1½  cups whole wheat pastry flour
½  teaspoon salt
2  teaspoons double-acting baking powder
1  cup broken walnuts or pecans (optional)*
1¼  cups mashed banana
3  tablespoons vegetable oil
¼  cup honey
½  cup wheat germ
    Grated zest of ½ lemon
2  teaspoons butter

**1.** Preheat oven to 350°F.
**2.** Sift flour, salt, and baking powder together. Add nuts and mix well until coated with flour.
**3.** Add banana, oil, honey, wheat germ, and lemon zest. Mix just until ingredients are combined.
**4.** Butter 4½- by 9-inch loaf pan or use nonstick loaf pan. Batter will be stiff; spread evenly in pan. Bake for about 45 minutes.

*Yield: 18 ½-inch slices*

| Nutritive values per ½-inch-thick slice serving: | CAL | CHO (gm) | PRO (gm) | FAT (gm) |
|---|---|---|---|---|
| | 134 | 23 | 2 | 6 |

| Food exchanges per ½-inch-thick slice serving: | 1 BREAD, 1 FRUIT, ½ FAT |
|---|---|

*If no nuts are used, subtract 36 calories, 4 grams of fat, and ½ FAT per slice.

# High-Protein Three-Grain Bread

*This wonderful recipe comes from Jane Brody's Good Food Book. It looks like a lot of work, but it really isn't. It just takes several hours to rise while you do something else! Actual preparation time is 20–25 minutes. If you can't get soy flour, use whole wheat flour.*

$2\frac{1}{2}$ cups boiling water
1 cup rolled oats (regular or quick, not instant)
$\frac{3}{4}$ cup nonfat dry milk
$\frac{1}{2}$ cup soy flour
$\frac{1}{4}$ cup wheat germ
$\frac{1}{4}$ cup honey
1 teaspoon salt
3 tablespoons vegetable oil
$\frac{1}{2}$ cup warm water (105–115°F)
2 packages (2 scant tablespoons) active dry yeast
1 tablespoon sugar
$5\frac{1}{2}$–6 cups whole wheat flour, preferably stone-ground

1. Preheat oven to 375°F.
2. In a very large bowl, combine the boiling water, oats, dry milk, soy flour, wheat germ, honey, salt, and oil. Cool the mixture to warm.
3. Place the warm water in a small bowl and add the yeast and sugar, stirring to dissolve them. Let the mixture stand for about 10 minutes or until the yeast starts to bubble.
4. Add the yeast mixture and $2\frac{1}{2}$ cups of the whole wheat flour to the oat mixture. Beat this for 2 minutes and then add enough of the remaining flour to form a dough that is easy to handle.
5. Turn the dough out onto a lightly floured board and knead it for about 10 minutes or until it is smooth and elastic. Place the dough in a large greased bowl, turning the dough to coat the top. Cover the bowl with a

dish towel and let the dough rise in a warm draft-free place until it has doubled in bulk, about 1½ hours.

6. Punch down the dough and divide in half. Flatten each half into a rectangle about 18 inches long and 8 inches wide. Starting from the short end, roll up each rectangle, pressing with your fingertips to seal the loaf as you go. Seal the ends and place each loaf in a greased loaf pan, about 9 by 5 by 3 inches. Cover the pans with a dish towel and let the loaves rise until they have doubled in bulk, about 1 hour.

7. Bake the bread for about 35–40 minutes or until the loaves sound hollow when tapped.

*Yield: 2 loaves*

| Nutritive values per ½-inch-thick slice serving: | CAL | CHO (gm) | PRO (gm) | FAT (gm) |
|---|---|---|---|---|
| | 113 | 21 | 4 | 1 |

Food exchanges per ½-inch-thick slice serving:       1½ BREAD

# Whole Grain Irish Soda Bread

*I also serve this at dinner, and it's a big hit.*

> 1¼ cups whole wheat flour
> 1½ cups unbleached white flour
> ¼ cup each wheat germ and brown sugar
> ½ teaspoon salt
> 2 teaspoons each baking soda and double-acting baking powder
> 1½ cups low-fat buttermilk
> 2 tablespoons diet margarine, melted
> ½ cup currants or raisins

1. Preheat oven to 375°F.
2. In a bowl, stir together all dry ingredients.
3. Stir in buttermilk and margarine until batter is blended but still lumpy.
4. Fold in currants or raisins.
5. Spoon batter into buttered and flour-dusted 8-inch round pan; do not smooth the surface.
6. Bake for 40–45 minutes or until a pick inserted in the center comes out clean. Cool bread in the pan for 10 minutes, then turn out on a wire rack. Serve warm, cooled, or sliced and toasted.

*Yield: 1 8-inch round loaf (16 wedges)*

| Nutritive values per 1-wedge serving: | CAL | CHO (gm) | PRO (gm) | FAT (gm) |
|---|---|---|---|---|
| | 121 | 23 | 3 | 2 |

Food exchanges per 1-wedge serving:           1½ BREAD, 1 FAT

# Refrigerator Bran Muffins*

*The sugar in this recipe adds up to only 1 teaspoon per muffin. More importantly, they're filled with fiber, which slows down the rise of blood sugar. The best news is that this batter will keep in your refrigerator, tightly covered,*

---

*For all the muffin recipes, I prefer to use nonstick muffin pans. You may also use paper muffin cups, or if necessary, lightly greased pans.

*for up to 4 weeks. You can bake muffins as you need them so that they're always fresh.*

  1  cup whole bran cereal, such as All Bran or Bran Buds
  1  cup boiling water
  ½  cup safflower oil
  ¼  cup light or dark brown sugar
  ¼  cup honey
  1  apple, grated
  2  carrots, grated
  2  eggs
  2  cups low-fat buttermilk
  2½  cups whole wheat flour
  2½  teaspoons baking soda
  ½  teaspoon salt
  1½  cups oatmeal (regular or quick, not instant)
  ½  cup wheat germ

1. In a 2- or 3-quart container with a cover, stir together the bran cereal and boiling water. Let stand for 10 minutes.
2. In another bowl, combine the oil, sugar, honey, apple, and carrots. Beat the eggs into the mixture. Mix in the buttermilk.
3. Combine the bran mixture and the oil mixture.
4. In another bowl, combine flour, baking soda, salt, oatmeal, and wheat germ. Slowly mix them into the bran mixture. Cover and refrigerate for several hours or overnight.
5. You can bake these muffins as needed in a 400°F oven for 20–25 minutes, until browned and a toothpick inserted in the center comes out clean.

*Yield: 24 muffins*

| Nutritive values per 1-muffin serving: | CAL | CHO (gm) | PRO (gm) | FAT (gm) |
|---|---|---|---|---|
| | 134 | 20 | 3.3 | 5 |

Food exchanges per 1-muffin serving:      1 BREAD, ½ FRUIT, 1 FAT

# Applesauce Muffins

*Applesauce makes these muffins delectably moist without overloading them with fat.*

$1\frac{1}{4}$ cups unsweetened applesauce
1 large egg
2 tablespoons oil
2 tablespoons honey
1 cup whole wheat flour (regular or pastry)
1 cup unbleached white flour
2 teaspoons double-acting baking powder
$\frac{3}{4}$ teaspoon baking soda
$\frac{1}{2}$ teaspoon ground cinnamon
$\frac{1}{4}$ teaspoon ground nutmeg
$\frac{3}{4}$ cup raisins

1. Preheat oven to 375°F.
2. In a large bowl, beat together the applesauce, egg, oil, and honey. Set the bowl aside.
3. In a medium bowl, combine the whole wheat and white flours, baking powder, baking soda, cinnamon, and nutmeg. Add this to the applesauce mixture, stirring just to moisten the dry ingredients. Stir in the raisins and divide the batter among 12 muffin cups.
4. Bake the muffins for 20 minutes.

### *Yield: 12 muffins*

| Nutritive values per 1-muffin serving: | CAL | CHO (gm) | PRO (gm) | FAT (gm) |
|---|---|---|---|---|
| | 128 | 23 | 3 | 2 |

Food exchanges per 1-muffin serving:      1 BREAD, 1 FRUIT, $\frac{1}{2}$ FAT

# Blueberry Muffins

*Brennan loves these blueberry muffins.*

2 cups whole wheat pastry flour
2 tablespoons sugar
1 tablespoon double-acting baking powder
¼ teaspoon ground cinnamon
¼ teaspoon ground nutmeg
1½ cups fresh or frozen blueberries, thawed
and drained
1 cup unsweetened orange juice
¼ cup diet margarine, melted
1 whole egg
1 egg white
1 teaspoon grated orange zest

**1.** Preheat oven to 400°F.
**2.** Combine the first 5 ingredients in a large bowl. Fold in blueberries. Make a well in the center of the mixture.
**3.** Combine orange juice, margarine, egg, egg white, and orange zest. Add to the dry ingredients. Stir just until moistened.
**4.** Fill muffin cups ⅔ full. Bake for 20–25 minutes, until golden.

*Yield: 16 muffins*

| Nutritive values per 1-muffin serving: | CAL | CHO (gm) | PRO (gm) | FAT (gm) |
|---|---|---|---|---|
| | 88 | 16 | 2 | 2 |

Food exchanges per 1-muffin
serving:                       1 BREAD, ½ FAT

# Orange Cottage Cheese Muffins

1½ cups unbleached white flour
½ cup buckwheat or whole wheat flour
1 cup yellow cornmeal (preferably stone-ground)
4½ teaspoons double-acting baking powder
¼ teaspoon salt
6 packets artificial sweetener (equal to ¼ cup sugar)
2 eggs
1 cup low-fat cottage cheese
¾ cup low-fat buttermilk
¼ cup fresh orange juice
2 teaspoons grated orange zest
⅓ cup oil
2 tablespoons raisins

1. Preheat oven to 400°F.
2. In a large bowl, combine the flours, cornmeal, baking powder, salt, and sweetener; mix well.
3. In a small bowl, beat eggs lightly; mix in the cottage cheese, buttermilk, orange juice, zest, oil, and raisins.
4. Make a well in the center of the flour mixture and add liquid ingredients all at once. Stir with a fork just enough to blend ingredients.
5. Fill muffin cups ⅔ full. Bake in a 400°F oven until golden brown, about 20 minutes.
6. Turn out of cups and serve hot or cool, or wrap airtight and refrigerate or freeze. To reheat muffins, wrap in foil and place in a 350°F oven for 15 minutes if chilled, 25 minutes if frozen.

*Yield: 24 muffins*

| Nutritive values per 1-muffin serving: | CAL | CHO (gm) | PRO (gm) | FAT (gm) |
|---|---|---|---|---|
| | 89 | 11 | 4 | 3 |

Food exchanges per 1-muffin serving:  1 BREAD, ½ FAT

# Oat Bran Muffins

*This recipe comes from the Oat Bran cereal box and is very good. Oat Bran is one hot cereal both my boys will eat, and its soluble fiber helps lower cholesterol in the blood. It also has the highest protein content of any plant protein other than soybeans.*

2¼ cups Oat Bran cereal
2 tablespoons brown sugar
¼ cup chopped nuts
¼ cup golden raisins
1 tablespoon double-acting baking powder
½ teaspoon salt
¾ cup skim milk
2 eggs, beaten
2 tablespoons honey
2 tablespoons vegetable oil

1. Preheat oven to 425°F.
2. Combine cereal, brown sugar, nuts, raisins, baking powder, and salt.
3. Add milk, eggs, honey, and oil; mix just until dry ingredients are moistened.
4. Fill muffin cups ¾ full. Bake 15–17 minutes or until golden brown.

*Yield: 12 muffins*

| Nutritive values per 1-muffin serving: | CAL | CHO (gm) | PRO (gm) | FAT (gm) |
|---|---|---|---|---|
| | 123 | 18 | 5 | 5 |

Food exchanges per 1-muffin serving: 1 BREAD, ½ lean MEAT, 1 FAT

# Lemon Muffins

1 cup unbleached white flour
1 cup whole wheat pastry flour
2 tablespoons sugar
½ teaspoon salt
⅔ cup skim milk
⅓ cup fresh lemon juice
1 teaspoon grated lemon zest
¼ cup vegetable oil
1 medium egg
2 tablespoons golden raisins

1. Preheat oven to 400°F.
2. Mix dry ingredients.
3. Combine remaining ingredients. Mix together with dry ingredients. Stir with fork. *Do not beat.* Batter will be lumpy.
4. Fill muffin cups ⅔ full. Bake 20–25 minutes.

*Yield: 12 muffins*

| Nutritive values per 1-muffin serving: | CAL | CHO (gm) | PRO (gm) | FAT (gm) |
|---|---|---|---|---|
| | 110 | 15 | 2 | 4 |

| Food exchanges per 1-muffin serving: | 1 BREAD, 1 FAT |
|---|---|

# JAMS AND FRUIT SAUCES
## Strawberry Jam

1 envelope sugar-free strawberry-flavored
  gelatin (1.3-ounce size)
1 cup boiling water
2 cups sliced fresh strawberries
  Grated zest of 2 oranges
  Grated zest of 1 lemon

**1.** In a small heatproof bowl, combine gelatin and boiling
water, stirring until gelatin is completely dissolved.
**2.** Stir in strawberries and grated orange and lemon zest.
**3.** Allow to cool, then pour into glass jar. Cover and chill
at least 1 hour before serving.

*Yield: 2 cups*

| Nutritive values per 1-tablespoon serving: | CAL | CHO (gm) | PRO (gm) | FAT (gm) |
|---|---|---|---|---|
| | 3 | 0 | 0 | 0 |

Food exchanges per 1-tablespoon
serving:                          Up to ¼ cup FREE

# Blueberry Jam Spread

1 teaspoon unflavored gelatin
¼ cup water
2 cups fresh or frozen blueberries
½ cup water
1 teaspoon fresh lemon juice
6 packets artificial sweetener (Equal)

1. Combine gelatin and ¼ cup water, stirring well. Set aside.
2. Combine blueberries, ½ cup water, and lemon juice in a medium saucepan. Bring to a boil, reduce heat, and simmer, uncovered, 8 minutes, stirring frequently.
3. Remove saucepan from heat and add gelatin, stirring well until gelatin is dissolved. Let cool for 10 minutes and stir in sweetener.
4. Cool to room temperature. Pour into glass jars and cover tightly. Chill 4–6 hours or until mixture is thoroughly chilled. Store in refrigerator for up to 1 month.

*Yield: 2 cups*

| Nutritive values per 1-tablespoon serving: | CAL | CHO (gm) | PRO (gm) | FAT (gm) |
|---|---|---|---|---|
| | 5 | 0 | 0 | 0 |

Food exchanges per 1-tablespoon serving:           Up to ¼ cup FREE

# Microwave Peach Jam

4 cups frozen, unsweetened sliced peaches, thawed
5 tablespoons powdered fruit pectin
1 tablespoon fresh lemon juice
¾ teaspoon ground mace
4 packets artificial sweetener (Equal)

1. Mash peaches with a potato masher.
2. Combine peaches with pectin, lemon juice, and mace in a deep 2-quart casserole.

**3.** Cover with casserole lid and microwave on HIGH for 2 minutes. Stir well.
**4.** Cover and microwave an additional 3–4 minutes.
**5.** Cool for 10 minutes and stir in sweetener. Pour into freezer containers; cover and freeze.
**6.** To serve, let jam thaw in refrigerator. Store jam in freezer up to 1 year or in refrigerator up to 1 month.

*Yield: 2 cups*

| Nutritive values per 1-tablespoon serving: | CAL | CHO (gm) | PRO (gm) | FAT (gm) |
|---|---|---|---|---|
| | 5 | 0 | 0 | 0 |

| Food exchanges per 1-tablespoon serving: | Up to ½ cup FREE |
|---|---|

# Fresh Blueberry Sauce

*This is very good over pancakes, French toast, and waffles. Brennan especially likes it.*

> 1  tablespoon cornstarch
> ½  cup water
> 1  tablespoon fresh lemon juice
> ¼  teaspoon ground mace
> 2  cups fresh blueberries
> 3  packets artificial sweetener (Equal)

**1.** Combine cornstarch, water, lemon juice, and mace in a small saucepan.
**2.** Add blueberries; bring to a boil. Reduce heat and simmer 1–2 minutes, stirring constantly, until clear and thickened. Stir in sweetener. Serve sauce warm over pancakes.

*Yield: 2 cups*

| Nutritive values per ¼-cup serving: | CAL | CHO (gm) | PRO (gm) | FAT (gm) |
|---|---|---|---|---|
| | 24 | 6 | 0 | 0 |

| Food exchanges per ¼-cup serving: | Up to ¼ cup FREE |
|---|---|

# Applesauce

*You can buy unsweetened applesauce now, but there's nothing as good as homemade.*

 4 medium cooking apples (about 1½ pounds)
 ½ cup unsweetened apple juice
 ¼ teaspoon ground cinnamon
 ⅛ teaspoon ground nutmeg

1. Peel, core, and cut apples into wedges; combine apples and apple juice in a saucepan.
2. Cook, uncovered, over medium-low heat 10–15 minutes or until apples are tender, stirring occasionally to break up apples.
3. Stir in spices. Add more water, if needed, to achieve desired consistency. Serve warm or chilled.

*Yield: 8 ⅓-cup servings*

| Nutritive values per ⅓-cup serving: | CAL | CHO (gm) | PRO (gm) | FAT (gm) |
|---|---|---|---|---|
| | 48 | 12 | 0 | 0 |

Food exchanges per ⅓-cup serving: 1¼ FRUIT

# Lunch

Lunchtime for children with diabetes can be a dilemma for parents. Usually it boils down to whether to let your child eat the school lunch like most of his or her friends or take the old brown bag. It's a hard decision to make because there are so many variables. We've done a little of everything.

The most difficult part of school lunches is giving up complete control over the food your child is served. Especially if your child is newly diagnosed (the first year is the roughest), a natural fear and protectiveness can hold you in its power. When deciding how to handle lunch, keep a few things in mind:

Your child is a child first and a diabetic second. As much as is possible, it is very important to allow the child to lead a normal life, to be like "all the other kids." Diabetes is a train that takes you for a lifelong ride. The risk of controlling a child too tightly in childhood is that the child may get to her teens and say, "That's it. I've had enough of this diet-and-shot routine. Now I'll do it my way."

It is important to let your child take some responsibility for her diabetes as early as possible. That includes her making some bad choices now and then. If you're blood-testing, your child will be able to see the consequences of a poor choice, and you can discuss what might have been better. To apply that to lunch, your child might decide to eat the fruit salad served with the school lunch, not fully realizing that it's not the same as the apple you packed as a substitute. Her after-school blood sugar will tell the tale, and she will understand next time. (By the way, she may still make the same choice. Only this time maybe she'll just eat a bite or two—just to be like the "other kids.")

You can formulate whatever plan suits your child's needs.

My son, Brennan, started by taking a lunch. First it was a lunch pail decorated with cartoon characters and a little thermos. As he got older, he started having the school lunch with everyone else because he didn't want to be different. Then we were able to get the monthly lunch menu, and I would send a bag lunch on days when the menu seemed inappropriate or it included something he didn't like. Lately he's been complaining about the food and wants to start taking his lunch again.

Getting a lunch menu plan from the school and going over it with your child gives you the broadest choice and helps both you and your child to think ahead. Simply mark off the lunches that seem inappropriate and plan to send a bag lunch on those days, as I did with Brennan.

Your child's brown bag or lunch box can be packed with anything from sandwiches to soups, stews, salads, and cut-up fresh vegetables and fruits. Brennan's current favorite lunch is a baked chicken breast with carrot sticks. You could add some homemade cookies and a piece of fruit to complete the exchanges. Little boxes of raisins are good for snacks to pack with lunch. Weight Watchers also makes dried apple snacks in foil pouches that are equal to one FRUIT.

The possibilities are endless when you have the right containers. Soups and stews stay steaming hot in those little individual-serving thermos jars. Tupperware makes a good lunch pail that has containers to hold sandwiches, drinks, anything moist like fruit salad, etc. Brennan likes to put a Tupperware glass of Crystal Light in the freezer overnight. The next morning he snaps the lid on, and by noon the drink has thawed but is still cold.

Any container with watertight, snap-on lids will work for the recipes in this chapter. However, some of these recipes won't do well sitting in a lunch pail for several hours. Tuna Melts, Mini Pizzas, and Sloppy Joes can be really unappealing if they're not served hot. They also get soggy after sitting around for a while.

Make a list with your child of all the brown bag possibilities and special favorites that will travel well. This gives your child a sense of control over his diet and gives you one place to look for menu possibilities. Make sure it includes choices for each of the exchanges in your child's lunch.

Now, about the recipes in this chapter. A wide selection of soups is included here because they can be made ahead and are very good for diabetics for several reasons. The soup recipes in this chapter are very low in fat and generally high in fiber. They give you more nutrition for fewer calories, and they are also filling. Soups containing vegetables are often eaten willingly by children who turn up their noses at the same vegetables presented on a dinner plate. Any of these soups can also be a good addition to dinner. Quite a few of them are almost a full meal of exchanges and make a satisfying main course accompanied by whole grain bread and fresh fruit for dessert.

It's much better to make homemade stock than to use canned. It's less expensive, for one thing, and you can make it almost totally fat-free and low in sodium. The easiest approach is to save leftover bones from chicken, turkey, and beef. (I find pork and lamb a little strong-flavored.) Have a bag in the freezer that holds the bones. Whenever it gets full, dump them into a pot and cover with water. Bring to a boil and then reduce heat to simmer. Add some cut-up onion, carrots, and celery. Simmer, covered, for a few hours. Let cool and place in the refrigerator. Skim all the fat that solidifies on the top. Strain the remaining broth and refrigerate. Freeze it if you won't be using it in a week or so.

You *can* use canned stock for the soup recipes that call for homemade stock. Try getting the new low-sodium stocks. Instead of adding extra salt, try adding fresh lemon juice or mild vinegar to any soup to give it extra zip.

Next, there are recipes for a few sandwiches, some main course dishes that adapt well to brown-bagging, and some salads. Macaroni and cheese and baked beans are good hot choices; pair them with cut-up vegetables and fruit. The potato salad and coleslaw are low-fat versions that you can use and season to your family's taste.

Most children have very strong opinions about the way sandwiches should be made, so it seemed presumptuous to include more than a few sandwich recipes. Sandwiches will, no doubt, be a mainstay of your child's homemade lunches, however, so the list below shows calories and exchanges for some common sandwich fillings. This is not by any means a complete list. Choose luncheon meats that emphasize 90–95 percent fat-free, preferably made from chicken or turkey. Try not to use only store-bought cold cuts for sandwiches. They're high in salt, sometimes have added sugar, and some are preserved with nitrates. Home-cooked chicken or turkey breast makes a great sandwich. Unsalted peanut butter is now available in many supermarkets. Try it. Your child probably won't notice the difference. For further reference, I highly recommend *The Diabetic's Brand-Name Food Exchange Handbook*, by Andrea Barrett (Running Press, Philadelphia, 1984).

## SANDWICH FILLINGS

TUNA: Solid White in Water
½ can (3½ ounces)                    120 calories/2 lean MEAT

TUNA: Chunk Light in Water
½ can (3½ ounces)                    120 calories/2 lean MEAT

TURKEY: Luncheon Meat or Turkey Sausage
Louis Rich (1 slice)                 40–60 calories/½ lean MEAT,
                                     ½ FAT

HAM
Oscar Mayer 95% FAT FREE             25 calories/½ lean MEAT
  (1 slice)

SALAMI
Hebrew National beef, sliced     90 calories/$\frac{1}{2}$ lean MEAT, 1$\frac{1}{2}$ FAT
   (1 ounce)

CHICKEN
Weaver white-meat roll     40 calories/$\frac{1}{2}$ lean MEAT
   (1 ounce)

PEANUT BUTTER
Smuckers Natural     200 calories/1 lean MEAT, 3 FAT
   (2 tablespoons)

JAM
Smuckers Low Sugar     32 calories/1 FRUIT
   Strawberry or Grape Jam
   (4 teaspoons)

CHEESE
American, Monterey Jack, or     110 calories/1 lean MEAT, 1 FAT
   Swiss (1 ounce)

FRANKFURTERS: The best choices, if you must serve them, are chicken and turkey franks. All wieners and franks are very high in sodium.
Weaver Chicken (1 frank)     120 calories/1 lean MEAT, 1$\frac{1}{2}$ FAT
Louis Rich Turkey (1 frank)     100 calories/1 lean MEAT, 1 FAT
(All the beef franks have 2–3$\frac{1}{2}$ FAT exchanges per frank.)

# LUNCH MENU IDEAS

These will need to be altered to fit your child's diet plan, but they should give you some ideas. (Check the index to locate recipes.)

## MENU 1

Corn Chowder     2 BREAD, $\frac{1}{2}$ medium-fat MEAT
8 ounces skim milk     1 MILK
Carrot and celery sticks     1 or 2 VEGETABLE
   (as much as desired)
$\frac{2}{3}$ cup strawberries     1 FRUIT

**TOTAL:** 2 BREAD, 1 FRUIT, 1 MILK, $\frac{1}{2}$ medium-fat MEAT, 1–2 VEGETABLE

## MENU 2

| | |
|---|---|
| Minestrone | 3 BREAD, 1 lean MEAT |
| 8 ounces skim milk | 1 MILK |
| 1 piece fruit or small box raisins (2 tablespoons) | 1 FRUIT |

**TOTAL:** 3 BREAD, 1 FRUIT, 1 MILK, 1 lean MEAT

## MENU 3

| | |
|---|---|
| 2 Mini Pizzas | 2 BREAD, 3 medium-fat MEAT, 1 VEGETABLE |
| ½ Stuffed Baked Apple (from Breakfast chapter) | 1 FRUIT |
| Carrot and celery sticks (as much as desired) | 1 or 2 VEGETABLE |

**TOTAL:** 2 BREAD, 1 FRUIT, 3 medium-fat MEAT, 2–3 VEGETABLE

## MENU 4

| | |
|---|---|
| 1 Open-Faced Tuna Melt | 1 BREAD, 3 lean MEAT |
| ½ cup Coleslaw or | ½ VEGETABLE, trace FAT |
| Special Fruited Coleslaw | ½ FRUIT, 1 VEGETABLE |
| 1 orange | 1 FRUIT |
| 8 ounces skim milk | 1 MILK |
| 1 Oatmeal Cookie (from Snack chapter) | ½ BREAD, ½ FAT |

**TOTAL:** 1½ BREAD, 1–1½ FRUIT, 1 MILK, 3 lean MEAT, ½–1 VEGETABLE, ½ FAT

## MENU 5

| | |
|---|---|
| Vegetable Soup (1⅓ cups) | 1 BREAD, 2 VEGETABLE |
| 1 Pita Pocket | 1 BREAD, 2 lean MEAT, 1 VEGETABLE |
| Fruit salad (homemade) (½ cup of any fruit combination) | 1 FRUIT |
| 8 ounces skim milk | 1 MILK |

**TOTAL:** 2 BREAD, 1 FRUIT, 1 MILK, 2 lean MEAT, 3 VEGETABLE

# LUNCH EXCHANGES

Use this list as a quick reference when planning lunch menus. A glance at the right-hand column should give you ideas of what to serve for certain exchanges called for in your child's diet plan. The recipes are listed here in the same order as they appear in the chapter.

| | |
|---|---|
| Egg Drop Soup | Up to 2 cups FREE |
| Minestrone | 3 BREAD, 1 lean MEAT |
| Navy Bean Soup | 1 BREAD, 1 lean MEAT, 1 VEGETABLE |
| Matzo Ball Soup | 2 lean MEAT, 1 VEGETABLE |
| Matzo Balls | ½ BREAD |
| Manhattan Clam Chowder | ½ BREAD, 1½ lean MEAT, 1 VEGETABLE |
| Corn Chowder | 2 BREAD, ½ medium-fat MEAT |
| Vegetable-Beef Soup | 2 BREAD |
| Split Pea Soup | 1 BREAD, 1 lean MEAT, 1 VEGETABLE |
| Vegetable Soup | 1 BREAD, 2 VEGETABLE |
| Lentil Soup | 1 BREAD, 3 VEGETABLE |
| Potato and Turnip Soup | ½ BREAD, 2 VEGETABLE |
| Greek Lemon Soup | ½ lean MEAT |
| Open-Faced Tuna Melts | 1 BREAD, 3 lean MEAT, 1 VEGETABLE |
| Pita Pockets | 1 BREAD, 2 lean MEAT, 1 VEGETABLE |
| Mini Pizzas | 1 BREAD, 1½ medium-fat MEAT |
| Sloppy Joes | 1 BREAD, 2 lean MEAT, 1 VEGETABLE |
| Baked Macaroni and Cheese | 1 BREAD, 1½ medium-fat MEAT |
| Baked Beans | 1 BREAD, ½ lean MEAT, 1 VEGETABLE |
| Turkey Chili | 1 BREAD, 3 lean MEAT, 1 VEGETABLE |
| Chili Deluxe with Vegetables | 1 BREAD, 2 lean MEAT, 2 VEGETABLE |
| New Potato Salad | 1½ BREAD, 1 FAT |
| German Potato Salad | 1 BREAD, 1 VEGETABLE, ½ FAT |
| Coleslaw | 1 VEGETABLE, trace FAT |
| Special Fruited Coleslaw | 1 FRUIT, 2 VEGETABLE |

# Recipes

## SOUPS
## Egg Drop Soup

*This soup is good for lunch with a sandwich or good before a Chinese-style dinner entree like Beef and Snow Peas (see index for recipe).*

 4 cups homemade chicken stock
 ¼ cup sliced green onion (¼-inch pieces)
 1 whole egg
 1 egg white, slightly beaten
 1 teaspoon soy sauce

1. Bring chicken stock to boil in a large saucepan. Add onions.
2. Remove from heat; slowly pour in egg and egg white, stirring gently as you pour. Add soy sauce and serve.

**Variations**
1. Add peeled, thinly sliced fresh gingerroot for extra stock flavor, but caution everyone not to eat it—it's *hot!*
2. If you like, you can thicken the soup slightly with 2 teaspoons cornstarch mixed with 2 tablespoons cold water stirred into the boiling stock in step 1.

*Yield: 6 ⅔-cup servings*

| Nutritive values per ⅔-cup serving: | CAL | CHO (gm) | PRO (gm) | FAT (gm) |
|---|---|---|---|---|
| | 15 | 0 | 2 | 1 |
| Food exchanges per ⅔-cup serving: | Up to 3 servings (2 cups) FREE | | | |

# Minestrone

*An easy way to half-cook the beans for this recipe is to put ½ cup (dried) of each in a large pot and cover with water. Bring to a boil and then simmer for 30 minutes, adding more water if necessary. You can use any stock for this, though beef stock is traditional.*

2  quarts homemade stock
½  cup white wine
1  large onion, sliced thin
1  medium leek, sliced fine
2  cloves garlic, minced
2  medium carrots, sliced
2  medium unpeeled potatoes, cubed
1  green pepper, chopped
1  cup half-cooked dried navy beans
1  cup half-cooked dried garbanzos
1  cup half-cooked dried split peas
1  cup half-cooked dried lima beans
½  cup dried lentils
1  teaspoon oregano leaves
2  teaspoons basil leaves
1  teaspoon thyme leaves
1  bay leaf
   Dash cayenne pepper
1  teaspoon ground cumin
   Juice of 1 lemon
1  cup whole wheat elbow macaroni
1  cup green beans, cut into 1-inch pieces
2  small zucchini, sliced
1  cup chopped tomatoes (preferably fresh)
1  cup tomato puree
   Grated Parmesan cheese

1. Bring stock and wine to a boil in a large soup pot. Add onion, leek, garlic, carrots, potatoes, green pepper, navy beans, garbanzos, peas, lima beans, lentils, seasonings, and lemon juice. Cover and simmer for 30 minutes or until vegetables are very soft but still holding their shape.

**2.** Add macaroni and cook for five minutes.

**3.** Add green beans, zucchini, tomatoes, and puree and cook for another 10 minutes or until macaroni is tender. To serve, sprinkle with a little grated Parmesan cheese.

*Yield: 8 2-cup servings*

| Nutritive values per 2-cup serving: | CAL | CHO (gm) | PRO (gm) | FAT (gm) |
|---|---|---|---|---|
| | 261 | 49 | 14 | 1 |

Food exchanges per 2-cup serving:  3 BREAD, 1 lean MEAT

# Navy Bean Soup

1 cup each finely diced carrots and celery
½ onion, minced
1 clove garlic, minced
3½ cups water
1 cup tomato puree
1½ cups cooked navy beans
⅛ teaspoon freshly ground pepper
2 tablespoons chopped fresh parsley
¼ cup Parmesan cheese

**1.** In a 2-quart saucepan, combine carrots, celery, onion, garlic, water, and tomato puree and bring to a boil. Reduce heat and simmer until vegetables are tender, about 15 minutes.

**2.** Add beans, pepper, and parsley. Heat about 5 minutes longer. Sprinkle 2 teaspoons of cheese on each serving.

*Yield: 6 1¼-cup servings*

| Nutritive values per 1¼-cup serving: | CAL | CHO (gm) | PRO (gm) | FAT (gm) |
|---|---|---|---|---|
| | 130 | 20 | 8 | 2 |

Food exchanges per 1¼-cup serving:  1 BREAD, 1 lean MEAT, 1 VEGETABLE

# Matzo Ball Soup

*I love Matzo Ball Soup and so do my boys.*

1 chicken, about 4 pounds
2 quarts water
1 whole onion, peeled and quartered
2 carrots, sliced
4 stalks celery, including tops, coarsely chopped
  Juice of ½ lemon
2 sprigs fresh parsley
2 sprigs fresh dill
¼ teaspoon freshly ground pepper
1 teaspoon salt
  Matzo Balls (recipe follows)

**1.** Clean the chicken and place it in a deep soup pot. Add water and the remaining ingredients except Matzo Balls. Bring to a boil, then simmer, covered, until the chicken is tender, about 2 hours. Remove the chicken, strain the soup, and chill.

**2.** Skim off the fat that rises to the top of the chilled soup. Reserve the cooked chicken for other recipes, like Chinese Chicken Salad. Reheat soup and add Matzo Balls, cooking as directed in recipe.

*Yield: 8 1-cup servings*

| Nutritive values per 1-cup serving: | CAL | CHO (gm) | PRO (gm) | FAT (gm) |
|---|---|---|---|---|
| | 103 | 4 | 13 | 4 |

Food exchanges per 1-cup serving:                    2 lean MEAT, 1 VEGETABLE

# Matzo Balls

1  whole egg
2  egg whites
½  cup matzo meal
2  tablespoons finely minced onions
½  teaspoon ground cinnamon (optional)
1  tablespoon chopped fresh parsley
½  teaspoon salt (optional)
¼  teaspoon freshly ground white pepper
   Mixture of a little oil and water to lubricate
   hands

1. Beat the egg and egg whites. Fold in the matzo meal and seasonings; put mixture in refrigerator for 1 hour.
2. Mix a little oil and water to lubricate hands for forming balls. Form balls slightly larger than walnuts. Drop balls gently into boiling stock. Cover pot. Let simmer for 30 minutes. Remove from heat and let stand for 30 minutes.

*Yield: 10 medium-sized balls*

| Nutritive values per matzo ball: | CAL | CHO (gm) | PRO (gm) | FAT (gm) |
|---|---|---|---|---|
| | 37 | 5 | 2 | 1 |

Food exchanges per matzo ball:     ½ BREAD

# Manhattan Clam Chowder

- 1 tablespoon diet margarine
- 1 cup diced onions
- 8 ounces potatoes, cut into cubes
- 1 16-ounce can tomatoes
- 2 cups diced carrots
- 1 green pepper, chopped
- 2 cups bottled clam juice
- 1 cup diced celery
- 1 cup water
- 1 teaspoon thyme leaves
  Dash freshly ground pepper
- 2 10-ounce cans clams, drained
- 2 tablespoons or more chopped fresh parsley

**1.** In 4-quart saucepan, heat margarine until bubbly; add onions and cook until onions are translucent.
**2.** Add remaining ingredients except clams and parsley and bring to a boil. Reduce heat and simmer for 1 hour.
**3.** Add chopped clams and parsley and bring to a boil. Reduce heat and simmer 5 minutes longer.

*Yield: 8 1½-cup servings*

| Nutritive values per 1½-cup serving: | CAL | CHO (gm) | PRO (gm) | FAT (gm) |
|---|---|---|---|---|
| | 133 | 12 | 15 | 3 |

| Food exchanges per 1½-cup serving: | ½ BREAD, 1½ lean MEAT, 1 VEGETABLE |
|---|---|

# Corn Chowder

2 tablespoons diet margarine
1 small onion, minced
½ cup minced celery
1 tablespoon all-purpose flour
2¼ cups skim milk
2 10-ounce bags frozen corn
¼ teaspoon salt
¼ teaspoon ground white pepper
⅛ teaspoon ground thyme
Paprika

1. Melt margarine in a heavy 2-quart saucepan over medium heat; add onion and celery and sauté 5 minutes or until tender.
2. Stir in flour; cook over low heat 1 minute, stirring constantly.
3. Gradually add milk; cook over medium heat, stirring constantly, until thickened and bubbly. Stir in corn, salt, pepper, and thyme; simmer 20 minutes, stirring occasionally.
4. Just before serving, puree half the soup in blender or food processor. Return to saucepan and mix with remaining soup. To serve, ladle soup into bowls and sprinkle with paprika.

*Yield: 4 1¼-cup servings*

| Nutritive values per 1¼-cup serving: | CAL | CHO (gm) | PRO (gm) | FAT (gm) |
|---|---|---|---|---|
| | 191 | 33 | 8 | 3 |

Food exchanges per 1¼-cup
serving:                                   2 BREAD, ½ medium-fat MEAT

# Vegetable-Beef Soup

1 cup dried northern beans
1 cup dried split peas
3 quarts water
1 soup bone, split
2 large stalks celery, chopped
½ bunch fresh parsley, chopped
2 cloves garlic, diced fine
2 medium onions, chopped
2 medium potatoes, chopped
2 large carrots, sliced
1 large turnip, chopped
2 bay leaves
1 cup tomato puree
½ cup diced green pepper
½ cup diced sweet red pepper
1 cup cut-up fresh or frozen green beans
8 ounces broad noodles, broken into pieces
Paprika
1 teaspoon oregano
½ teaspoon rosemary
Dash Worcestershire sauce

1. Place beans and peas in bowl and add water to cover. Soak overnight. Drain.
2. Bring 3 quarts water to boil in stockpot. Add soup bone and simmer, covered, 3 hours. Remove soup bone.
3. To broth add drained beans and split peas, celery, parsley garlic, onions, potatoes, carrots, turnip, bay leaves, and tomato puree. Simmer, covered, about 2 hours or until legumes are tender. Add green and red pepper and green beans and cook 10–15 minutes, until tender. Add noodles and cook about 7 minutes or until noodles are tender. Add paprika to taste, oregano, rosemary, and Worcestershire. Remove bay leaves before serving.

*Yield: 12 1-cup servings*

| Nutritive values per 1-cup serving: | CAL | CHO (gm) | PRO (gm) | FAT (gm) |
|---|---|---|---|---|
| | 137 | 26 | 6 | 1 |

Food exchanges per 1-cup
serving:                                2 BREAD

# Split Pea Soup

    8  ounces dried split peas
    4  cups water
    ¾  cup chopped onion
    ½  cup chopped carrots
    ½  cup chopped lean ham
    ½  teaspoon ground celery seeds
    ¼  teaspoon salt
    ¼  teaspoon freshly ground pepper
    ¼  teaspoon marjoram leaves
    ⅛  teaspoon thyme leaves

**1.** Sort and wash peas; place in a Dutch oven. Add remaining ingredients and bring to a boil. Cover, reduce heat, and simmer 1 hour or until peas are tender.
**2.** Pour half of mixture into container of an electric blender or a food processor; process until smooth. Repeat with remaining mixture. Serve hot.

*Yield: 6 1-cup servings*

| Nutritive values per 1-cup serving: | CAL | CHO (gm) | PRO (gm) | FAT (gm) |
|---|---|---|---|---|
| | 157 | 25 | 12 | 1 |

Food exchanges per 1-cup
serving:                                1 BREAD, 1 lean MEAT,
                                        1 VEGETABLE

# Vegetable Soup

*If you substitute canned stock, omit the salt.*

4 cups homemade chicken, beef, vegetable, or turkey stock
1 16-ounce can tomatoes
½ cup chopped onions
½ cup thinly sliced carrots
½ cup diagonally sliced celery
½ cup coarsely chopped green pepper
½ teaspoon salt
2 tablespoons fresh lemon juice
5 whole peppercorns
½ teaspoon basil leaves
¼ teaspoon hot pepper sauce
½ cup alphabet pasta or any other small pasta, uncooked

**1.** Combine all ingredients except pasta in a 3- to 4-quart pot. Bring to a boil. Cover and simmer gently for 1 hour. Stir occasionally to break up tomatoes into bite-sized pieces.
**2.** Add pasta and cook for 5–7 minutes, until done.

*Yield: 7 cups (5½ servings)*

| Nutritive values per 1⅓-cup serving: | CAL | CHO (gm) | PRO (gm) | FAT (gm) |
|---|---|---|---|---|
| | 116 | 24 | 5 | 0 |

| Food exchanges per 1⅓-cup serving: | 1 BREAD, 2 VEGETABLE |
|---|---|

# Lentil Soup

4 cups homemade chicken stock
2 cups water
¼ cup red wine
1 cup dried lentils
½ cup long-grain brown rice
1 16-ounce can tomatoes, chopped
1 bay leaf
¼ cup chopped fresh parsley
1 teaspoon ground cumin
1 carrot, sliced
1 onion, chopped
1 celery stalk, sliced
2 garlic cloves, minced or pressed
  Juice of ½ lemon
1 bunch (6–8 ounces) fresh spinach, cleaned
  and stemmed

1. Combine all ingredients except spinach in a 3- to 4-quart saucepan and bring to a boil. Reduce heat and cover. Simmer for 20–25 minutes or until lentils and rice are tender.
2. Cut spinach across the leaves in long, thin shreds. Add to soup and simmer for 5 minutes. Remove bay leaf and serve.

*Yield: Approximately 8 1-cup servings*

| Nutritive values per approximate 1-cup serving: | CAL | CHO (gm) | PRO (gm) | FAT (gm) |
|---|---|---|---|---|
| | 144 | 27 | 9 | 0 |

Food exchanges per approximate
1-cup serving:            1 BREAD, 3 VEGETABLE

# Potato and Turnip Soup

*This low-fat, hearty soup is from* Jane Brody's Good Food Book.

1 small onion, sliced thin ($\frac{1}{4}$ cup)
2 small white turnips (about $\frac{1}{3}$ pound), peeled and sliced thin
1 pound potatoes (about 3 medium), peeled and sliced thin
3 cups homemade chicken broth
1 cup skim milk
$\frac{1}{2}$ teaspoon ground nutmeg
Freshly ground pepper to taste
$\frac{1}{4}$ cup evaporated skim milk

1. In a large saucepan, combine the onion, turnips, potatoes, and broth. Bring the soup to a boil, reduce the heat, partially cover the pan, and simmer the soup until the vegetables are tender, about 10 minutes.
2. Transfer the vegetables and cooking liquid to a blender or food processor (in batches, if necessary) and puree them.
3. Just before serving, return the puree to a saucepan and heat the puree over a moderately low flame. Add the skim milk, nutmeg, and pepper and heat the soup to just below boiling. Stir in the evaporated milk and serve.

*Yield: 6 1-cup servings*

| Nutritive values per 1-cup serving: | CAL | CHO (gm) | PRO (gm) | FAT (gm) |
|---|---|---|---|---|
| | 84 | 17 | 4 | 0 |

Food exchanges per 1-cup serving:   $\frac{1}{2}$ BREAD, 2 VEGETABLE

# Greek Lemon Soup

*Here's the Greek version of egg drop soup, with the added tang of lemon and herbs.*

4 cups homemade chicken stock
2 tablespoons long-grain rice
1 whole egg, beaten
1 egg white, beaten
2 tablespoons fresh lemon juice
1 tablespoon chopped fresh parsley
½ teaspoon oregano leaves
Dash freshly ground black pepper

1. Bring stock to a boil. Add rice, cover, and turn heat down to simmer for 15–20 minutes, until rice is tender.
2. Mix egg, egg white, and lemon juice. Slowly pour egg mixture into stock, stirring gently, and simmer for 2–3 minutes.
3. Add herbs and pepper. Serve.

*Yield: 4 servings*

| Nutritive values per 1-cup serving: | CAL | CHO (gm) | PRO (gm) | FAT (gm) |
|---|---|---|---|---|
| | 32 | 3 | 4 | 1 |

| Food exchanges per 1-cup serving: | ½ lean MEAT |
|---|---|

# SANDWICHES

For exchange information on some common sandwich fillings, refer to the list in the introduction to this chapter.

## Open-Faced Tuna Melts

1 7-ounce can tuna, packed in water
2 tablespoons diet mayonnaise
2 tablespoons fresh lemon juice
2 tablespoons low-fat cottage cheese
2 teaspoons Dijon mustard
2 tablespoons finely minced red onion (optional)
4 slices whole grain bread, toasted
4 slices fresh tomato (optional)
½ cup grated American or Cheddar cheese

1. Drain tuna. Flake with a fork.
2. Combine next 5 ingredients and mix into tuna.
3. Spoon equal amounts on each slice of bread. Top with tomato and 2 tablespoons cheese each. Broil in toaster oven or broiler until cheese bubbles.

*Yield: 4 servings*

| Nutritive values per serving: | CAL | CHO (gm) | PRO (gm) | FAT (gm) |
|---|---|---|---|---|
| | 212 | 16 | 19 | 8 |

Food exchanges per serving:  1 BREAD, 3 lean MEAT

# Pita Pockets

*Pita bread comes in a whole wheat variety that is tasty and nutritious. Each round can be cut in half and filled like a little pocket—a nice change from regular sandwiches. You can use turkey, tuna, or ground beef instead of the chicken listed here. Pita pockets can also hold the same ingredients used for tacos with much less mess.*

½ pound cooked shredded chicken
2 tablespoons diced red onion
½ cup diced celery
½ green or red sweet pepper, diced
1 tablespoon diet mayonnaise
2 tablespoons plain nonfat yogurt
2 teaspoons fresh lemon or lime juice
1 teaspoon Dijon mustard
　Pinch cayenne pepper
2 pita rounds
　Shredded lettuce and alfalfa sprouts
　(optional)

1. Mix first 9 ingredients. Refrigerate for 30 minutes or longer.
2. Cut pitas in half and fill each pocket with one-quarter of the chicken mixture. Add a little lettuce or alfalfa sprouts if desired.

*Yield: 4 pocket sandwiches*

| Nutritive values per serving: | | CHO (gm) | PRO (gm) | FAT (gm) |
|---|---|---|---|---|
| | CAL | | | |
| | 189 | 18 | 18 | 5 |

Food exchanges per serving: 1 BREAD, 2 lean MEAT, 1 VEGETABLE

# Mini Pizzas

*I normally don't serve frankfurters because they contain preservatives, but kids do like them. If you prefer not to serve them, make the pizzas without them and subtract ½ medium-fat MEAT exchange.*

    4  English muffins, split
    1  8-ounce can tomato sauce
       Dried oregano and dried basil
    4  turkey frankfurters, sliced
    8  teaspoons Parmesan cheese
    8  slices (¼-inch thick) part-skim mozzarella
       cheese

1. Spread each muffin half with 2 tablespoons tomato sauce. Top with a pinch each of oregano and basil.
2. Put sliced ½ frankfurter onto each muffin. Top with 1 teaspoon Parmesan cheese and 1 slice mozzarella. Toast under broiler or in toaster oven or microwave until cheese melts and bubbles.

*Yield: 8 pizzas*

| | CAL | CHO (gm) | PRO (gm) | FAT (gm) |
|---|---|---|---|---|
| Nutritive values per 1-pizza serving: | 218 | 18 | 13 | 11 |

Food exchanges per 1-pizza serving:

1 BREAD, 1½ medium-fat MEAT, ½ VEGETABLE

# Sloppy Joes

1 pound lean ground beef
½ onion, chopped fine
2 stalks celery, including leaves, chopped
½ green pepper, chopped
2 medium fresh tomatoes, pureed in blender
2 tablespoons fresh lemon juice
½ teaspoon dry mustard
2 teaspoons Worcestershire sauce
3 whole wheat hamburger buns, split and
toasted

1. Put meat in heavy frying pan and cook over medium heat until brown. Drain in a colander to rid of all fat.
2. Combine remaining ingredients, except hamburger buns, in pan and sauté over medium heat for 5 minutes. Add meat, reduce heat, and simmer, covered, for 15 minutes more. Stir frequently.
3. Serve on hamburger bun half.

*Yield: 6 servings*

| Nutritive values per serving (including ½ cup meat mixture): | CAL | CHO (gm) | PRO (gm) | FAT (gm) |
|---|---|---|---|---|
| | 196 | 18 | 17 | 6 |

Food exchanges per serving
(including ½ cup meat mixture):    1 BREAD, 2 lean MEAT,
1 VEGETABLE

# MAIN COURSE LUNCHES
# Baked Macaroni and Cheese

1 cup whole wheat or regular elbow macaroni
2 eggs, beaten
1 cup skim milk
1 cup low-fat cottage cheese
1/4 cup shredded extra-sharp Cheddar cheese
1/2 teaspoon dry mustard
1/4 teaspoon ground white pepper
1 tablespoon dry bread crumbs

1. Preheat oven to 350°F.
2. Cook macaroni according to package instructions, without salt. Drain.
3. Combine macaroni with next 6 ingredients. Spoon into a 1-quart baking dish that has been wiped with a little bit of oil. Sprinkle with bread crumbs. Bake for 1 hour.

*Yield: 6 ⅔-cup servings*

| Nutritive values per ⅔-cup serving: | CAL | CHO (gm) | PRO (gm) | FAT (gm) |
|---|---|---|---|---|
| | 179 | 17 | 12 | 7 |

Food exchanges per ⅔-cup serving:

1 BREAD, 1½ medium-fat MEAT

# Baked Beans

1 pound dried northern beans
  Cold water
½ cup chopped center-cut ham (bone, fat, and skin removed)
1 cup chopped onions
1 6-ounce can tomato paste
1 teaspoon salt
2 tablespoons Dijon mustard
1 tablespoon vinegar
2 tablespoons blackstrap molasses
8 packets artificial sweetener (equal to ⅓ cup sugar)

1. Wash and sort beans. Add cold water, cover, and soak overnight.
2. The next day, drain and cover with fresh cold water. Bring to boil and simmer for 30 minutes. Preheat oven to 250°F.
3. Drain and reserve bean liquid. Mix beans with remaining ingredients and place in a covered baking dish.
4. Bake for 6–9 hours in oven or use crock pot on low setting. Add reserved bean water if they become dry. Uncover for the last hour of cooking.

*Yield: 6 cups (18 servings)*

| Nutritive values per ⅓-cup serving: | CAL | CHO (gm) | PRO (gm) | FAT (gm) |
|---|---|---|---|---|
| | 126 | 19 | 8 | 2 |

Food exchanges per ⅓-cup serving:   1 BREAD, ½ lean MEAT, 1 VEGETABLE

# Turkey Chili

*This is an easy, very tasty dish, and turkey is much lower in fat than beef or pork. You can use strips of leftover roast turkey instead of uncooked ground turkey, about 4 cups, and add it to the beans for the last 10 minutes of cooking time. To use dried beans, cover 1 cup of beans with water and simmer for 1 hour or until tender; they will yield 2 cups cooked.*

2 pounds ground turkey
1 medium onion, chopped
2 cloves garlic, pressed or minced
1 16-ounce can whole tomatoes, undrained
1 8-ounce can tomato sauce
2 cups homemade chicken stock
1 fresh Anaheim chili, seeded and chopped (optional)
2 tablespoons chili powder or more to taste
1 teaspoon ground cumin
1 teaspoon paprika
½ teaspoon freshly ground pepper
2 green apples, peeled and chopped
2 cups cooked red or pinto beans *or* 1 16-ounce can, drained

1. Combine all ingredients except apples and beans in large pot. Bring to a boil, reduce heat, cover, and simmer for 30 minutes. Stir frequently to break up the turkey and tomatoes.
2. Add apples and simmer covered for another 20 minutes. Add beans and cook 10 minutes longer.

*Yield: 8 1⅓-cup servings*

| Nutritive values per 1⅓-cup serving: | CAL | CHO (gm) | PRO (gm) | FAT (gm) |
|---|---|---|---|---|
| | 261 | 20 | 25 | 0 |

| Food exchanges per 1⅓-cup serving: | 1 BREAD, 3 lean MEAT, 1 VEGETABLE |
|---|---|

# Chili Deluxe with Vegetables

*These are sneaky vegetables, the kind your kids hardly notice. They add nutrition and fiber while playing second fiddle to the meat and beans.*

> 1 cup dried pinto beans
> 1 pound lean ground beef
> 1 large onion, chopped
> 2 cloves garlic, pressed or minced
> 2 tablespoons chili powder
> 1 teaspoon paprika
> ¼ teaspoon ground cloves
> ½ teaspoon ground cumin
> ½ teaspoon ground coriander
> ½ teaspoon oregano leaves
> ½ teaspoon basil leaves
> 1 8-ounce can tomato sauce
> 1 16-ounce can tomatoes
> 1 cup homemade beef or chicken stock
> 1 cup diced green pepper
> 1 cup grated carrots
> 1 cup diced celery

1. Cook beans in water to cover for 1 hour or until just tender. Drain and set aside.
2. Sauté beef, onion, and garlic for 10 minutes. Drain off all fat.
3. Add seasonings, tomato sauce, tomatoes, and stock and simmer for 1 hour. Add more stock if necessary.
4. Add green pepper, carrots, and celery and cook, covered, for 20 minutes, until tender. Add beans and heat for 10 minutes.

*Yield: 8 1-cup servings*

| Nutritive values per 1-cup serving: | CAL | CHO (gm) | PRO (gm) | FAT (gm) |
|---|---|---|---|---|
| | 219 | 25 | 19 | 5 |

| Food exchanges per 1-cup serving: | 1 BREAD, 2 lean MEAT, 2 VEGETABLE |
|---|---|

# SALADS
# New Potato Salad

2 pounds small red new potatoes
½ small red onion, chopped
1 green pepper, seeded and chopped
2 hard-cooked eggs, chopped
¼ cup minced fresh parsley
1 cup plain nonfat yogurt
2 tablespoons diet mayonnaise
3 tablespoons minced fresh dill *or* 1
    tablespoon dried dill weed
2 tablespoons Dijon mustard
1 tablespoon fresh lemon juice
½ teaspoon freshly ground pepper
  Paprika

1. Steam the potatoes, unpeeled, until they are just tender when pierced with a fork. If small, halve them. If medium-size, quarter them. Use a sharp knife and try not to pull the skin off.
2. Add the onion, green pepper, eggs, and parsley.
3. Combine yogurt, mayonnaise, dill, mustard, lemon juice, and pepper and pour over vegetables. Mix gently. Sprinkle with paprika and refrigerate.

*Yield: 8 ⅔-cup servings*

| Nutritive values per ⅔-cup serving: | CAL | CHO (gm) | PRO (gm) | FAT (gm) |
|---|---|---|---|---|
| | 149 | 21 | 5 | 5 |

Food exchanges per ⅔-cup
serving:                                    1½ BREAD, 1 FAT

# German Potato Salad

*This is an Italian version of German potato salad because it uses pancetta instead of bacon. Pancetta is a bacon-type meat that is preserved with salt, not nitrates, and can be found in Italian delis. You can use bacon if you absolutely have to, but try to get pancetta.*

 4 medium potatoes, peeled
 1 medium onion, chopped
 3 stalks celery, chopped
 2 teaspoons olive oil
 ½ cup water
 6 tablespoons cider vinegar
 1 tablespoon all-purpose flour
 2 packets artificial sweetener (equal to 4 teaspoons sugar)
 ½ teaspoon freshly ground pepper
 2 tablespoons minced fresh parsley
 2 ounces pancetta, chopped, sautéed until crisp, and drained

1. Cook potatoes in boiling water to cover until tender, about 25–30 minutes. Drain.
2. Fry onion and celery in olive oil until onion is slightly browned. Add water, vinegar, flour, sweetener, and pepper. Cook and stir over medium heat until thickened, about 10 minutes.
3. Slice potatoes and place in bowl. Add parsley and pancetta. Pour sauce over and mix gently.

*Yield: 4 cups (8 servings)*

| Nutritive values per ½-cup serving: | CAL | CHO (gm) | PRO (gm) | FAT (gm) |
|---|---|---|---|---|
| | 108 | 20 | 4 | 3 |

Food exchanges per ½-cup serving:          1 BREAD, 1 VEGETABLE, ½ FAT

# Coleslaw

4 cups shredded green cabbage
2 cups shredded carrots
¾ cup thinly sliced green onions
⅔ cup cider vinegar
1 tablespoon Dijon mustard
1½ teaspoons paprika
1 teaspoon mustard seeds
½ teaspoon celery seeds
½ teaspoon freshly ground pepper
½ cup nonfat yogurt
½ cup low-fat cottage cheese

1. Combine cabbage, carrots, and onions in a large bowl.
2. Combine remaining ingredients in a blender or food processor and whirl just until smooth. Pour over vegetables and refrigerate overnight.

*Yield: 8 1-cup servings*

| Nutritive values per 1-cup serving: | CAL | CHO (gm) | PRO (gm) | FAT (gm) |
|---|---|---|---|---|
| | 49 | 6 | 4 | 1 |

| Food exchanges per 1-cup serving: | 1 VEGETABLE, trace FAT |
|---|---|

# Special Fruited Coleslaw

1   small green cabbage (approximately 1½ pounds), chopped
1   20-ounce can unsweetened crushed pineapple, undrained
2   medium apples, diced
1½  cups grated carrots
1   cup chopped celery
½   cup golden raisins
1   cup nonfat yogurt
1   teaspoon grated lemon zest
1   teaspoon fresh lemon juice

Combine all ingredients in a large bowl and toss. Cover and refrigerate overnight.

*Yield: 11 1-cup servings*

| Nutritive values per 1-cup serving: | CAL | CHO (gm) | PRO (gm) | FAT (gm) |
|---|---|---|---|---|
| | 90 | 20 | 3 | 0 |

Food exchanges per 1-cup serving:                1 FRUIT, 2 VEGETABLE

# Snacks

Snack time can be easy or frustrating, depending on your child's tastes and flexibility. If her snack exchanges are a BREAD and a FRUIT, it's easy to put 10 Wheat Thins and an apple in front of her. Your child, however, may not feel like eating Wheat Thins and an apple. That's why many recipes in this chapter combine BREAD and FRUIT or BREAD and MEAT exchanges in the form of nutritious, special snacks and treats.

No two days are exactly alike for a child. It is always best to stick as closely as possible to your child's prescribed diet plan, but, as parents, we learn things about our children's reactions to different foods that no doctor or dietitian can predict in advance. For a long time, Brennan has had very different day-to-day afternoon blood sugars, so a set amount of food in the afternoon is not a good idea in Brennan's case. This is why blood-testing has become so important to us, as it should be for your child. Brennan may come home really hungry and yet have a 180 blood sugar. Then I try to fill him up with vegetables and dip and a noncaloric drink. Other days, he's 130 but has soccer or basketball practice. That's a good time for an extra treat like frozen yogurt or ice cream.

Concerning frozen desserts, many of the yogurt and even ice cream parlors now make a very healthy version that is low-fat, sweetened with fructose, and uses unsweetened berries for toppings. An interesting note on ice cream and such is that, of all the parents I talked to, none mentioned that ice cream raised their child's blood sugar unreasonably. Quite the opposite, in fact: several said ice cream was fine but other foods, like pizza, sent blood sugars through the roof. I asked Tina Leeser, the nutritionist for this book, why. She hypothesized that many of the less expensive ice creams are made with guar, which is a gel-like fiber that holds the food in the stomach longer. That way, the food takes longer to metabolize and raises the blood sugar more slowly. Nutrition researcher Phyllis Crapo noted that even ice creams made without guar rated lower than many foods on the glycemic index. Researchers aren't sure why.

Snack time is time to think of good nutrition, not just feeding your child anything that's a bread or a fruit exchange. The closer to a natural state a food is, the better. Whole grain bread is far better than crackers, whole fruit is better than juice, etc. The usual good sense should prevail. All the snacks in this chapter are good sources of nutrition.

This chapter is divided into three sections: beverages, savory snacks, and sweet snacks. Generally, you'll find the quickest recipes to prepare in the earlier pages of this chapter. Shakes are a snap to prepare, and the savory snacks resemble simple appetizers.

Diet sodas present a bit of a dilemma at our house. I would prefer that my boys not drink sodas—diet or otherwise. They add nothing to their overall health. They often contain added chemicals and sodium, and phosphates, which can interfere with absorption of calcium when ingested in large amounts. Instead of banning them, I encourage moderation. I try to limit our consumption of diet sodas as much as possible, so we use flavored mineral water and Crystal Light for noncaloric drinks. There are now several sugar-free, noncarbonated drink mixes on the market. (The healthiest beverage, of course, is water, but I know my kids want something flavored most of the time.)

Many of the recipes in the sweet snacks section would normally pass as desserts. They are listed in this chapter, rather than as dinner recipes, because I would rather serve a treat-type snack in the morning or afternoon when a child is active.

# SNACK EXCHANGES

Use this list as a quick reference when planning snack menus. A glance at the right-hand column should give you ideas of what to serve for certain exchanges called for in your child's diet plan. The recipes are listed here in the same order as they appear in the chapter.

| | |
|---|---|
| Pineapple Shake | 1 FRUIT, ½ MILK |
| Chocolate Shake | 1 MILK |
| Grape Soda | 1 FRUIT |
| Spiced Tea | Less than 1 cup FREE; 1 cup = ½ FRUIT |
| Dip for Vegetables or Sort-of Sour Cream | 1 lean MEAT |
| Bean Dip | 1⅓ BREAD |
| Peanut Dip | 1 FAT |
| Homemade Tortilla Chips | 1 BREAD, ½ FAT |
| Sesame Nachos | ½ BREAD, 1 FAT |
| Popcorn Treat | 1½ BREAD, ½ FRUIT, ½ FAT |
| Meatball Snacks | 1 lean MEAT |
| Devilish Eggs | ½ medium-fat MEAT |
| Peach Whip | ½ FRUIT |
| Frozen Banana | ½ BREAD, 1 FRUIT |
| Frozen Fruit Pops | ⅔ FRUIT |
| Orange Sherbert | 1 FRUIT, ½ MILK |
| Pineapple Sherbert | 1½ FRUIT |
| Carrot and Raisin Salad | ½ FRUIT, 1 VEGETABLE, trace FAT |
| Apple Salad | 1 FRUIT, trace FAT |
| Baked Custard | ½ MILK, ½ lean MEAT |
| Brennan's Rice Pudding | 1 BREAD, ½ lean MEAT, ½ FAT |
| Peanut Butter Cookies | 1 BREAD, ½ FRUIT, 2 FAT |
| Chocolate Chip Cookies | 1 BREAD, 1½ FAT |
| "Wholesome" Brownies | 1 FRUIT, 1½ FAT |

| | |
|---|---|
| Apple Crunch | 1 BREAD, 1 FRUIT, 1 FAT |
| Oatmeal Cookies | ½ BREAD, ½ FAT |
| Cherry Pie | ⅔ BREAD, 1 FRUIT, 1 FAT |
| Lean Pie Crust | ½ BREAD, ½ FAT |
| Quick Banana Cream Pie | 1 BREAD, ½ FRUIT, ½ MILK, 1 FAT |
| Graham Cracker Crust | 1 BREAD, 1 FAT |
| Fresh Peach Pie | 1 BREAD, 1½ FRUIT, 1 FAT |
| Whole Grain Pastry Shell | 1 BREAD, 1 FAT |
| Applesauce Bran Squares | 1 BREAD, 1½ FAT |
| Carrot Snack Cake | 1 BREAD, ½ FRUIT, 1 FAT |
| Vanilla Cheesecake | ½ BREAD, 1 MILK, 2 FAT |
| Oatmeal Bread | 1 BREAD, ½ FRUIT, ½ FAT |
| Zucchini Bread | ⅔ BREAD, 1 FAT |

# Recipes

## BEVERAGES

## Pineapple Shake

*A child any age can help you make this shake. Toddlers can count out the pineapple pieces and help measure the flavoring. Older children can whip it up themselves.*

½   cup skim milk
10   pieces unsweetened canned pineapple chunks and small amount of juice (approximately ½ cup)
1   packet artificial sweetener (Equal)
1   teaspoon pineapple flavoring
1   teaspoon coconut flavoring

Blend all ingredients in blender or food processor. Blend until smooth.

*Yield: 1 serving*

| Nutritive values per serving: | CAL | CHO (gm) | PRO (gm) | FAT (gm) |
|---|---|---|---|---|
| | 80 | 16 | 4 | 0 |
| Food exchanges per serving: | 1 FRUIT, ½ MILK | | | |

# Chocolate Shake

*Commercial sugar-free chocolate milk mixes are now available, or you can make this one. Better yet, teach your child to make it!*

>     1  cup skim milk
>     1  tablespoon unsweetened cocoa
>     1  packet artificial sweetener (Equal)
>   3-4  ice cubes

Place ingredients in blender or food processor and blend at high speed until frothy and thickened. Serve immediately.

*Yield: 1 serving*

| Nutritive values per serving: | CAL | CHO (gm) | PRO (gm) | FAT (gm) |
|---|---|---|---|---|
| | 100 | 15 | 9 | 0 |

Food exchanges per serving:     1 MILK


# Grape Soda

>   ¼  cup unsweetened grape juice
>   1  cup sparkling water

**Variations**

**1.** To make apple soda, replace ingredients above with ⅓ cup unsweetened apple juice and 1 cup lemon-lime-flavored diet soda.

**2.** To make orange soda, use ½ cup unsweetened orange juice and 1 cup lemon-lime-flavored diet soda.

*Yield: 1 serving*

| Nutritive values per serving: | CAL | CHO (gm) | PRO (gm) | FAT (gm) |
|---|---|---|---|---|
| | 40 | 10 | 0 | 0 |

Food exchanges per serving:     1 FRUIT

# Spiced Tea

*I first had this in Canada and thought it was a very refreshing drink, hot or iced. This version uses herb tea since children certainly don't need caffeine.*

6   cups boiling water
8   whole cloves
3   cinnamon sticks
6   bags herb orange/spice tea
    (noncaffeinated)
1   6-ounce can unsweetened pineapple juice
1   cup unsweetened orange juice
    Juice of ½ lemon
4   packets artificial sweetener (Equal)

Simmer the water and spices for 5 minutes. Add tea bags and remove from heat. Steep for 5 minutes. Remove tea bags and spices. Add juices and sweetener. Serve immediately or refrigerate in covered pitcher. Reheat or serve iced.

*Yield: 8 1-cup servings*

| Nutritive values per 1-cup serving: | CAL | CHO (gm) | PRO (gm) | FAT (gm) |
|---|---|---|---|---|
| | 16 | 4 | 0 | 0 |

| Food exchanges per 1-cup serving: | Less than 1 cup FREE; 1 cup = ½ FRUIT |
|---|---|

# SAVORY SNACKS

# Dip for Vegetables, or Sort-of Sour Cream

*Use this recipe as a base for dips or as a replacement for sour cream on baked potatoes. My kids don't notice any difference between this and the higher-fat sour cream dips. Brennan loves to add the herbs and spices. A dip like this is great after school, surrounded by whatever vegetables your child likes. Be inventive and try Chinese pea pods, fresh green beans, jicama strips, green or red pepper strips, broccoli and cauliflower flowerets, as well as the old standbys of carrots, celery, and cucumber. Your child may develop a liking for a new vegetable if it's served with a tasty dip.*

> ½ cup plain nonfat yogurt
> ½ cup low-fat cottage cheese
> 1 tablespoon fresh lemon juice or white
>    vinegar

Combine the ingredients in a blender or food processor and blend briefly, until smooth. Chill an hour or two, after adding whatever herbs and spices you desire, or use the following variations.

**Variations**
1. Add 2 tablespoons chopped fresh parsley, 1 clove finely minced garlic, and dash cayenne pepper to dip mixture before chilling.
2. Add 2 tablespoons chopped fresh dill, chives, cilantro, basil, or tarragon (or 2 teaspoons dried) or a combination of these herbs to dip mixture before chilling.
3. Add 2 tablespoons Parmesan cheese and 2 tablespoons chopped fresh chives to dip mixture before chilling.

*Yield: 1 cup*

| Nutritive values per 3-tablespoon serving: | CAL | CHO (gm) | PRO (gm) | FAT (gm) |
|---|---|---|---|---|
| | 43 | 1 | 7 | trace |

Food exchanges per 3-tablespoon serving:                1 lean MEAT

# Bean Dip

*Serve this dip with Tortilla Chips (recipe follows). You can buy canned bean dip, but making your own is easy. It's also healthier because it will be much lower in sodium. Legumes raise the blood sugar slowly, so they are good for diabetics.*

2  cups cooked pinto beans *or* 1 16-ounce can pinto beans
2  tablespoons finely chopped canned or fresh green chilies, seeded, *or* 1 fresh jalapeño, seeded and minced (optional)
1  tablespoon fresh lemon juice
1  tablespoon red wine vinegar
1  teaspoon chili powder
1  teaspoon ground cumin
1  tablespoon minced fresh cilantro or parsley

Place all ingredients in a blender or food processor and blend until smooth. Serve at room temperature.

*Yield: 2 cups*

| Nutritive values per 2-tablespoon serving: | CAL | CHO (gm) | PRO (gm) | FAT (gm) |
|---|---|---|---|---|
| | 42 | 22 | 2 | trace |

Food exchanges per 2-tablespoon serving:                1⅓ BREAD

# Peanut Dip

*The first time I tried this recipe I thought it would be either awful or wonderful. It's wonderful! Serve it with celery sticks, cucumber slices, jicama strips, and/or fresh pineapple chunks. (You can use canned pineapple, but fresh is much better.) Peanut butter is a concentrated source of calories, but, according to our knowledge of glycemic reaction, the fat content should assist in slowing the rise of blood sugar. The fiber in the fresh vegetables and fruit will also help to slow blood sugar rise. Remember also that peanut oil is a monounsaturated fat and may actually help cholesterol problems. For those reasons, an extra serving shouldn't be a problem for an active child. I say all of this because 2 tablespoons might look like a paltry serving. Put it in the center of a small plate and surround it with raw vegetables and ½ cup pineapple chunks (1 FRUIT). It's a filling snack.*

⅓  cup smooth or crunchy natural peanut
    butter
2   packets artificial sweetener (Equal)
¼   cup fresh lemon juice
2   tablespoons tomato-based chili sauce or
    catsup
½   teaspoon soy sauce
    Dash cayenne pepper

Mix all ingredients together and serve at room temperature.

*Yield: ⅔ cup*

| Nutritive values per 2-tablespoon serving: | CAL | CHO (gm) | PRO (gm) | FAT (gm) |
|---|---|---|---|---|
| | 52 | 2 | 2 | 4 |

| Food exchanges per 2-tablespoon serving: | 1 FAT | | | |

# Homemade Tortilla Chips

*These chips are superior to commercial chips for two healthy reasons—lower sodium and much lower fat.*

> 10  6-inch fresh corn tortillas
> 2  tablespoons peanut or vegetable oil

1. Preheat oven to 350°F.
2. Using a pastry brush, lightly coat one side of each tortilla with oil. Use a sharp knife to cut the tortillas, stacked together, into halves, quarters, then eighths.
3. Spread chips on nonstick baking pans. Bake for 10 minutes or until crisp and beginning to brown.

*Yield: 80 chips*

| Nutritive values per 10-chip serving: | CAL | CHO (gm) | PRO (gm) | FAT (gm) |
|---|---|---|---|---|
| | 90 | 15 | 2 | 2 |

Food exchanges per 10-chip serving:          1 BREAD, ½ FAT

# Sesame Nachos

*Everybody loves these, and kids can easily make them on their own.*

> 4  Homemade Tortilla Chips (see previous recipe)
> 4  tablespoons grated Cheddar cheese
> 1  tablespoon unhulled sesame seeds

Top the chips with cheese and sesame seeds. Broil just until cheese melts, or use your toaster oven or microwave on medium for 1½–2½ minutes, just until cheese melts.

*Yield: 1 serving*

| Nutritive values per serving: | CAL | CHO (gm) | PRO (gm) | FAT (gm) |
|---|---|---|---|---|
| | 82 | 4 | 3 | 6 |

Food exchanges per serving:          ½ BREAD, 1 FAT

# Popcorn Treat

*This is a good, healthy after-school snack that can be made in larger quantities and stored in an airtight container at room temperature.*

1 cup plain popped popcorn (unsalted, preferably air-popped)
1 cup bite-size shredded wheat biscuits
2 tablespoons raisins
1 tablespoon dry-roasted sunflower seeds
½ teaspoon ground cinnamon

Mix first 4 ingredients. Sprinkle cinnamon over mixture and toss lightly.

*Yield: 2 cups (2 servings)*

| Nutritive values per 1-cup serving: | CAL | CHO (gm) | PRO (gm) | FAT (gm) |
|---|---|---|---|---|
| | 150 | 27 | 3 | 3 |

Food exchanges per 1-cup
serving:                                    1½ BREAD, ½ FRUIT, ½ FAT

# Meatball Snacks

*This is a variation of a recipe from* The Art of Cooking for the Diabetic, *by Katharine Middleton and Mary Abbott Hess (Contemporary Books, 1978).*

1 pound very lean ground beef
1 large egg, beaten
¼ cup tomato juice
¼ teaspoon ground nutmeg
1 teaspoon grated lemon zest
2 tablespoons fresh lemon juice
2 tablespoons wheat germ
1 slice fresh whole grain bread, finely crumbled

1. Preheat oven to 400°F.
2. Line a shallow baking pan with foil or use a nonstick pan.
3. Combine all ingredients and mix well. Form into tiny balls, using about 1 teaspoon of mixture per ball. Place 1 inch apart in pan. Bake 10 minutes.

*Yield: 80 meatballs (20 servings)*

| Nutritive values per 4-meatball serving: | CAL | CHO (gm) | PRO (gm) | FAT (gm) |
|---|---|---|---|---|
| | 51 | 1 | 5 | 3 |

Food exchanges per 4-meatball serving:  1 lean MEAT

# Devilish Eggs

*This is a good high-protein snack to serve occasionally with vegetables and dip. I recommend serving it only occasionally because the egg yolks are high in cholesterol.*

8  hard-cooked eggs
½  cup low-fat cottage cheese
1  tablespoon Dijon mustard
Dash hot red pepper sauce

1. Cut eggs in half lengthwise. Remove yolks.
2. Mash yolks with remaining ingredients and spoon mixture back into egg whites.

*Yield: 16 stuffed halves (8 servings)*

| Nutritive values per 1-piece serving: | CAL | CHO (gm) | PRO (gm) | FAT (gm) |
|---|---|---|---|---|
| | 39 | 0 | 4 | 3 |

Food exchanges per 1-piece serving:  ½ medium-fat MEAT

## SWEET SNACKS

# Peach Whip

*This recipe is from General Foods, the maker of Jell-O.*

¾ cup boiling water
1 4-serving package sugar-free orange or
  raspberry Jell-O
½ cup ice cubes
1 8-ounce can sliced peaches in juice or light
  syrup

1. Pour water into blender or food processor with gelatin. Blend until dissolved. Add ice cubes and stir until partially melted.
2. Drain peaches. Add to gelatin and blend until ice is melted and peaches are pureed. Pour into serving bowl or glasses. Chill about 2 hours, until set.

*Yield: 4 servings (approximately 2 cups)*

| Nutritive values per ½-cup serving: | CAL | CHO (gm) | PRO (gm) | FAT (gm) |
|---|---|---|---|---|
| | 24 | 5 | 1 | 0 |

| Food exchanges per ½-cup serving: | | |
|---|---|---|
| | ½ FRUIT | |

# Frozen Banana

*My kids love the frozen bananas we buy at amusement parks. Those are usually coated with chocolate, but these are good, too. Make several and have them ready for a snack.*

½  banana, peeled
2  tablespoons skim milk
¼  cup Grape Nuts cereal, crushed to crumbs
   Dash each ground cinnamon and ground
   nutmeg

1. Insert an ice cream stick deeply into the cut end of the banana.
2. Dip the banana in milk and roll in cereal crumbs and spices.
3. Wrap in plastic and freeze.

*Yield: 1 serving*

| Nutritive values per serving: | | CHO | PRO | FAT |
|---|---|---|---|---|
| | CAL | (gm) | (gm) | (gm) |
| | 68 | 16 | 1 | 0 |

Food exchanges per serving:        ½ BREAD, 1 FRUIT

# Frozen Fruit Pops

*Like most kids, mine love Popsicles, especially in the summer. These frozen fruit pops are so much better for your child than anything you can buy. They contain no added sugar and have the added benefit of fiber from the banana. Tupperware makes good frozen bar forms that I use all the time. Use the following recipe or ¼ cup unsweetened grape or orange juice in each form, which would equal 1 FRUIT. The exchanges below are based on ¼ cup per frozen fruit pop; ⅓ cup would be almost 1 FRUIT.*

> 1 cup mashed ripe banana
> 1 8-ounce can unsweetened crushed pineapple, undrained
> 1 cup unsweetened orange juice
> 2 teaspoons fresh lemon juice

1. Combine all ingredients and pour into 8- or 9-inch baking pan. Freeze until almost firm.
2. Spoon mixture into a mixing bowl and beat with an electric mixer until smooth and creamy. Spoon mixture into frozen bar forms. Freeze until firm.

*Yield: 12 frozen fruit treats*

| Nutritive values per frozen fruit pop: | CAL | CHO (gm) | PRO (gm) | FAT (gm) |
|---|---|---|---|---|
| | 28 | 7 | 0 | 0 |

| Food exchanges per frozen fruit pop: | ⅔ FRUIT |
|---|---|

# Orange Sherbert

> 1 6-ounce can orange juice concentrate
> 1½ cups skim milk
> ⅔ cup nonfat dry milk
> 1 teaspoon vanilla extract

1. Blend ingredients well and put in freezer until partially frozen—45 minutes to 1 hour.
2. Remove from freezer and beat until smooth. Return to freezer until frozen.

*Yield: 6 ½-cup servings*

| Nutritive values per ½-cup serving: | CAL | CHO (gm) | PRO (gm) | FAT (gm) |
|---|---|---|---|---|
| | 88 | 18 | 4 | 0 |

| Food exchanges per ½-cup serving: | | |
|---|---|---|
| | 1 FRUIT, ½ MILK | |

# Pineapple Sherbert

  8 ounces nonfat yogurt
  1 20-ounce can unsweetened crushed pineapple in juice
  4 packets artificial sweetener (Equal)
  ½ cup unsweetened orange juice

1. Combine all ingredients in blender or food processor. Whirl 1 minute, pour into shallow baking pan, and freeze until frozen 1 inch around edges.
2. Turn into chilled bowl and beat with electric or rotary beater until smooth, then freeze until set.
3. Allow to soften slightly at room temperature before serving.

*Yield: 8 ½-cup servings*

| Nutritive values per ½-cup serving: | CAL | CHO (gm) | PRO (gm) | FAT (gm) |
|---|---|---|---|---|
| | 73 | 16 | 1 | 0 |

| Food exchanges per ½-cup serving: | |
|---|---|
| | 1½ FRUIT |

# Carrot and Raisin Salad

*Some kids love this sort of dish, and some don't, but it's so nutritious that it's worth a try.*

- 4 medium carrots, grated
- ½ cup golden raisins
- ¼ cup nonfat yogurt
- ¼ cup low-fat cottage cheese
- 1½ teaspoons fresh lemon juice
- 1 packet artificial sweetener (Equal)
- ⅛ teaspoon cayenne pepper (optional)

1. Combine carrots and raisins.
2. Combine remaining ingredients in blender or food processor. Whirl until smooth. Stir into carrot mixture.

*Yield: 6 ½-cup servings*

| Nutritive values per ½-cup serving: | CAL | CHO (gm) | PRO (gm) | FAT (gm) |
|---|---|---|---|---|
| | 47 | 7 | 3 | 1 |

Food exchanges per ½-cup serving: ½ FRUIT, 1 VEGETABLE, trace FAT

# Chocolate Chip Cookies

*This recipe comes from* The New Diabetic Cookbook, *by Mabel Cavaiani (Contemporary Books, 1984).*

> 1 cup (2 sticks) diet margarine at room temperature
> ¼ cup sugar
> ¼ cup Brown SugarTwin
> 3 large egg whites at room temperature
> 1 tablespoon vanilla extract
> 2 cups unbleached white flour
> 1 teaspoon baking soda
> ¼ teaspoon salt
> ¼ cup water at room temperature
> ½ cup mini semisweet chocolate chips

1. Preheat oven to 375°F.
2. Cream margarine, sugar, and Brown SugarTwin at medium speed until light and fluffy. Add egg whites and vanilla to creamed mixture and beat at medium speed for 1 minute.
3. Stir together flour, soda, and salt to blend well. Add water to creamed mixture along with the flour mixture and mix at medium speed for 1 minute or until smooth.
4. Add chocolate chips to dough and mix lightly. Drop by tablespoonfuls onto cookie sheets that have been lined with aluminum foil or are nonstick. Press down lightly with fingers dipped in cold water to form a circle about 2 inches across. Bake about 12–15 minutes or until browned. (The cookies won't be crisp unless they are browned.)

*Yield: 44 cookies*

| Nutritive values per 2-cookie serving: | CAL | CHO (gm) | PRO (gm) | FAT (gm) |
|---|---|---|---|---|
| | 144 | 15 | 3 | 8 |

| Food exchanges per 2-cookie serving: | 1 BREAD, 1½ FAT |
|---|---|

# Baked Custard

1   12-ounce can evaporated skim milk
2   eggs, beaten slightly
1   egg white
2   tablespoons sugar
4   packets artificial sweetener (equal to 8
    teaspoons sugar)
1   teaspoon vanilla extract
½   teaspoon grated orange or lemon zest
¼   teaspoon ground nutmeg or mace

**1.** Preheat oven to 325°F.
**2.** Heat milk in the top of a double boiler over simmering water until surface begins to wrinkle.
**3.** Blend together the eggs, egg white, sugar, sweetener, vanilla, and zest. Add hot milk gradually, stirring to mix well.
**4.** Pour into 4 individual custard cups. Sprinkle with nutmeg. Set cups in a pan; pour hot water around cups to within ½ inch of tops of custard cups. Bake 50–60 minutes or until knife tip inserted in center of custard comes out clean. Chill several hours before serving.

*Yield: 4 ½-cup servings*

| Nutritive values per ½-cup serving: | CAL | CHO (gm) | PRO (gm) | FAT (gm) |
|---|---|---|---|---|
| | 87 | 6 | 9 | 3 |

Food exchanges per ½-cup serving:        ½ MILK, ½ lean MEAT

# Brennan's Rice Pudding

3 eggs
6 packets artificial sweetener (equal to ¼ cup sugar)
2 teaspoons vanilla extract
¼ teaspoon each ground cinnamon and ground nutmeg
2 cups evaporated skim milk
1 cup long-grain brown rice or white converted rice, cooked
¼ cup raisins

1. Preheat oven to 325°F.
2. Beat eggs. Mix in sweetener, vanilla, cinnamon, and nutmeg.
3. Add milk and mix thoroughly. Stir in rice and raisins. Pour into 2-quart soufflé dish. Place in shallow pan and pour hot water around soufflé dish to a depth of 1 inch. Bake for approximately 45 minutes.

*Yield: 8 ½-cup servings*

| Nutritive values per ½-cup serving: | CAL | CHO (gm) | PRO (gm) | FAT (gm) |
|---|---|---|---|---|
| | 113 | 15 | 9 | 2 |

Food exchanges per ½-cup serving:
1 BREAD, ½ lean MEAT, ½ FAT

# Peanut Butter Cookies

*These cookies contain only ½ teaspoon of sugar per cookie, and my boys love them.*

1½  cups sifted unbleached white flour
1½  teaspoons double-acting baking powder
½   teaspoon salt
¼   cup diet margarine
¼   cup brown sugar or fructose
½   cup smooth, natural peanut butter (no added sugar or hydrogenated oils)
1   teaspoon grated fresh orange zest
2   teaspoons vanilla extract
1   egg, well beaten
⅓   cup unsweetened orange juice
4   packets artificial sweetener (equal to 8 teaspoons sugar)

1. Preheat oven to 400°F.
2. Sift together flour, baking powder, and salt.
3. Cream together margarine, sugar, peanut butter, orange zest, and vanilla. Add egg, orange juice, and sweetener; blend well.
4. Add dry ingredients gradually; mix well after each addition.
5. Measure 1 level tablespoon dough for each cookie. Roll between hands to form ball. Place 2 inches apart on an ungreased cookie sheet; flatten with fork. Bake about 15 minutes. Store cookies in a tightly covered tin. These cookies have better flavor and texture 24 hours after baking.

*Yield: 24 cookies*

| Nutritive values per 2-cookie serving: | CAL | CHO (gm) | PRO (gm) | FAT (gm) |
|---|---|---|---|---|
| | 170 | 17 | 5 | 9 |

| Food exchanges per 2-cookie serving: | 1 BREAD, ½ FRUIT, 2 FAT |
|---|---|

# Apple Salad

*This easy and delicious salad is from* Jane Brody's Good Food Book.

### Salad
2 large red delicious apples, cored but unpeeled and cut into chunks
⅔ cup canned crushed unsweetened pineapple, drained, or fresh minced pineapple, juice reserved
⅓ cup diced celery
2 tablespoons raisins

### Dressing
3 tablespoons low-fat yogurt
2 teaspoons diet mayonnaise
1 tablespoon pineapple juice (reserved from pineapple)
⅛ teaspoon ground cinnamon

1. In a medium bowl, combine the salad ingredients.
2. In a small bowl, combine the dressing ingredients. Add the dressing to the fruit mixture and blend.

*Yield: 8 ½-cup servings*

| Nutritive values per ½-cup serving: | CAL | CHO (gm) | PRO (gm) | FAT (gm) |
|---|---|---|---|---|
| | 41 | 8 | 0 | 1 |

| Food exchanges per ½-cup serving: | | |
|---|---|---|
| | 1 FRUIT, trace FAT | |

# "Wholesome" Brownies

*These delicious brownies are courtesy of* Jane Brody's Good Food Book. *The oats and wheat germ add nutrition and high fiber, which slows down the rise of blood sugar. The sugar content is about 1 teaspoon per brownie. If you have any concern about the sugar content, please consult your dietitian or physician.*

1 6-ounce package (1 cup) semisweet chocolate chips
⅓ cup diet margarine
1 scant cup quick-cooking rolled oats
¼ cup wheat germ
⅓ cup nonfat dry milk
½ teaspoon double-acting baking powder
¼ teaspoon salt (optional)
½ cup chopped walnuts
2 eggs
¼ cup packed brown sugar
2 tablespoons white sugar
1 teaspoon vanilla extract

1. Preheat oven to 350°F.
2. In the top of a double boiler or in a small heavy saucepan over very low heat, melt the chocolate chips and the margarine. Remove the pan from the heat and stir the mixture until it is smooth. Set it aside.
3. In a medium bowl, combine the oats, wheat germ, dry milk, baking powder, salt, and nuts. Set the mixture aside.
4. In a large mixing bowl, beat the eggs and mix in the brown and white sugars and the vanilla until the mixture is thick. Stir in the melted chocolate mixture. Fold in the oats mixture until it is just blended. Pour the batter into a greased 8-inch square baking pan.
5. Bake the brownies for 20–25 minutes or until the top is crisp but a toothpick inserted in the center of the pan comes out slightly moist. Set pan on a rack to cool completely before cutting the brownies into 5 strips in each direction.

*Yield: 25 brownies*

| Nutritive values per 1-brownie serving: | CAL | CHO (gm) | PRO (gm) | FAT (gm) |
|---|---|---|---|---|
| | 111 | 10 | 2 | 7 |

Food exchanges per 1-brownie
serving:                                    1 FRUIT, 1½ FAT

# Apple Crunch

*This is a good alternative to apple pie and one my kids love. Lemon juice can be used instead of lime, but lime is more interesting.*

> 4 cups pared, sliced apples
> ¾ cup unsweetened orange juice
> 1 teaspoon fresh lime juice
> 1 teaspoon ground cinnamon
> 1 cup graham cracker crumbs
> 2 tablespoons wheat germ
> 2 tablespoons diet margarine

1. Preheat oven to 400°F.
2. Layer apples in 1-quart casserole. Combine juices and cinnamon and pour over apples.
3. Combine cracker crumbs and wheat germ with margarine and sprinkle over apples.
4. Cover with foil and bake for 25 minutes. Uncover and bake 5–10 minutes longer.

*Yield: 10 ⅓-cup servings*

| Nutritive values per ⅓-cup serving: | CAL | CHO (gm) | PRO (gm) | FAT (gm) |
|---|---|---|---|---|
| | 153 | 25 | 2 | 5 |

Food exchanges per ⅓-cup
serving:                                    1 BREAD, 1 FRUIT, 1 FAT

# Oatmeal Cookies

*These cookies are a good snack because the oatmeal provides protein and fiber to raise blood sugar slowly.*

⅓ cup raisins
¾ cup boiling water
¼ cup brown sugar
6 packets artificial sweetener (equal to ¼ cup sugar)
1 cup (2 sticks) diet margarine at room temperature
1 egg
2 egg whites
1 teaspoon vanilla extract
2 cups unbleached white flour
1½ teaspoons ground cinnamon
1 teaspoon double-acting baking powder
½ teaspoon baking soda
2 cups rolled oats (regular or quick, not instant)

1. Preheat oven to 375°F.
2. Combine raisins and boiling water and set aside to cool to room temperature.
3. Cream together sugar, sweetener, and margarine at medium speed until light and fluffy. Add egg, egg whites, and vanilla to creamed mixture and mix at low speed for 1 minute.
4. Stir together flour, cinnamon, baking powder, and soda to blend well.
5. Add oats to creamed mixture along with flour mixture, raisins, and liquid in which raisins were soaked. Mix at medium speed until flour is moistened.
6. Drop by heaping tablespoonfuls onto nonstick cookie sheets or sheets that have been lined with aluminum foil. Press down lightly with fingers dipped in cold water to form circles about 2 inches across. Bake for 10–12 minutes. Transfer from hot cookie sheet to wire rack to cool to room temperature.

*Yield: 3 dozen cookies*

| Nutritive values per 1-cookie serving: | CAL | CHO (gm) | PRO (gm) | FAT (gm) |
|---|---|---|---|---|
| | 74 | 10 | 2 | 3 |

Food exchanges per 1-cookie serving: ½ BREAD, ½ FAT

# Cherry Pie

*This is a good cherry pie recipe that I adapted from* The New Diabetic Cookbook, *by Mabel Cavaiani (Contemporary Books, 1984).*

2  16-ounce cans unsweetened red cherries, drained, liquid reserved
1  tablespoon cornstarch
18  packages artificial sweetener (Equal)
¼  teaspoon almond flavoring
1  teaspoon vanilla extract
½  teaspoon each ground cinnamon and mace
1  prebaked single-crust Lean Pie Crust (recipe follows)

**1.** Combine 1 cup reserved cherry liquid and cornstarch. Cook and stir over moderate heat until thickened and transparent and the starchy taste is gone. Remove from heat and add sweetener, almond flavoring, vanilla, spices, and cherries. Taste and add more sweetener, if desired. Cool to room temperature.
**2.** Spread filling evenly in crust. Let set at least 15 minutes. Cut into 8 equal portions.

*Yield: 1 9-inch pie (8 servings)*

| Nutritive values per serving: | CAL | CHO (gm) | PRO (gm) | FAT (gm) |
|---|---|---|---|---|
| | 124 | 20 | 2 | 4 |

Food exchanges per serving: ⅔ BREAD, 1 FRUIT, 1 FAT

# Lean Pie Crust

½ cup sifted unbleached white flour
¼ teaspoon salt
¼ teaspoon double-acting baking powder
¼ cup diet margarine at room temperature

1. Stir flour, salt, and baking powder together. Cut in margarine with fork or pastry blender and continue mixing until no pastry sticks to the sides of the bowl. Shape into a ball. Wrap and refrigerate for an hour or more.
2. Roll the dough out on a floured board. If prebaking, heat oven to 425°F and bake about 12 minutes or until golden.

*Yield: 1 single-crust 8- or 9-inch pie shell (8 servings)*

Nutritive values per serving:

| | CAL | CHO (gm) | PRO (gm) | FAT (gm) |
|---|---|---|---|---|
| | 50 | 7 | 1 | 2 |

Food exchanges per serving:    ½ BREAD, ½ FAT

# Quick Banana Cream Pie

*If you use the vanilla pudding mix, you might try adding ½ teaspoon extra vanilla for more flavor.*

1 Graham Cracker Crust (recipe follows)
1 envelope (.087 ounce) Bird's English Custard (my favorite) *or* 1 4-serving package sugar-free vanilla pudding mix
2 large *or* 3 medium firm-ripe bananas

1. Prepare the pie crust according to the recipe directions and chill.
2. Following the package directions, prepare the custard using artificial sweetener to replace the sugar, or prepare the sugar-free pudding mix.
3. Slice 1½ bananas into the bottom of the pie crust. Pour

pudding or custard over the top. Slice remaining ½ banana and arrange in circles over top. Chill for 2–3 hours.

*Yield: 8 servings*

| Nutritive values per serving of filling: | CAL | CHO (gm) | PRO (gm) | FAT (gm) |
|---|---|---|---|---|
| | 73 | 12 | 4 | 1 |

Food exchanges per serving of filling: ½ FRUIT, ½ MILK, trace FAT

| Total nutritive values per serving: | CAL | CHO (gm) | PRO (gm) | FAT (gm) |
|---|---|---|---|---|
| | 189 | 30 | 6 | 1 |

Total food exchanges per serving: 1 BREAD, ½ FRUIT, ½ MILK, 1 FAT

# Graham Cracker Crust

¾ cup graham cracker crumbs
2 tablespoons wheat germ
⅓ cup diet margarine

Blend crumbs, wheat germ, and margarine thoroughly with a fork or fingers. Press firmly into a nonstick 8- or 9-inch pie plate.

*Yield: 1 8- or 9-inch pie crust*

| Nutritive values per ⅛-crust serving: | CAL | CHO (gm) | PRO (gm) | FAT (gm) |
|---|---|---|---|---|
| | 116 | 18 | 2 | 4 |

Food exchanges per ⅛-crust serving: 1 BREAD, 1 FAT

# Fresh Peach Pie

*My mom, Dorothy Rosenberg, sent this lower-calorie recipe and it's great. I've provided the exchanges for the filling in case you want to use a different pastry recipe.*

> 2 tablespoons brown sugar
> 4 packets artificial sweetener (equal to 8 teaspoons sugar)
> 1 tablespoon cornstarch
> Juice of ½ lemon
> 1½ cups peeled and mashed fresh peaches
> 3 cups peeled and sliced fresh peaches
> Whole Grain Pastry Shell (recipe follows)

1. Combine sugar, sweetener, and cornstarch in a medium saucepan with juice and mashed peaches. Bring to a boil, reduce heat, and simmer about 5 minutes, until mixture is thickened, stirring constantly. Set aside to cool.
2. Place sliced peaches in pastry shell. Spoon cooled peach mixture over peaches and chill thoroughly.

*Yield: 8 servings*

| Nutritive values per serving of filling: | CAL | CHO (gm) | PRO (gm) | FAT (gm) |
|---|---|---|---|---|
| | 56 | 14 | 0 | 0 |

Food exchanges per serving of filling: 1½ FRUIT

| Total nutritive values per serving: | CAL | CHO (gm) | PRO (gm) | FAT (gm) |
|---|---|---|---|---|
| | 170 | 27 | 2 | 6 |

Total food exchanges per serving: 1 BREAD, 1½ FRUIT, 1 FAT

# Whole Grain Pastry Shell

*This pastry shell is very tasty and high in fiber. You could use it with any pie filling.*

¾  cup whole wheat pastry flour
½  cup quick-cooking oats (not instant)
1  tablespoon brown sugar
1  teaspoon ground cinnamon
½  cup diet margarine, melted
2  tablespoons water
   Vegetable oil

1. Preheat oven to 450°F.
2. Combine flour, oats, sugar, and cinnamon in a small bowl. Combine margarine and water; sprinkle over dry ingredients. Mix with a fork until mixture forms a ball.
3. Coat a 9-inch pie plate with vegetable oil; press whole wheat pastry mixture evenly and firmly into pie plate with lightly floured hands. Bake for 12–15 minutes; cool and fill.

*Yield: 1 9-inch pie shell*

| Nutritive values per ⅛-shell serving: | CAL | CHO (gm) | PRO (gm) | FAT (gm) |
|---|---|---|---|---|
| | 114 | 13 | 2 | 6 |

Food exchanges per ⅛-shell
serving:                              1 BREAD, 1 FAT

# Applesauce Bran Squares

*This recipe from* The New Diabetic Cookbook, *by Mabel Cavaiani (Contemporary Books, 1984), is very good and high in fiber.*

> 1 cup unbleached white flour
> ⅔ cup Bran Buds, All Bran, or 100% Bran
> ½ cup rolled oats (regular or quick, not instant)
> 2 tablespoons brown sugar
> ½ teaspoon baking soda
> 1 teaspoon double-acting baking powder
> 1 teaspoon ground cinnamon
> ¼ teaspoon ground cloves or nutmeg or mace
> ½ cup (1 stick) diet margarine at room temperature
> 2 large egg whites at room temperature
> 1 teaspoon vanilla extract
> 8 packets artificial sweetener (equal to ⅓ cup sugar)
> ⅓ cup chopped nuts
> 1 cup unsweetened applesauce at room temperature

1. Preheat oven to 375°F.
2. Place dry ingredients in mixer bowl and mix at low speed for 1 minute.
3. Add margarine, egg whites, vanilla, sweetener, nuts, and applesauce to flour mixture and mix at medium speed for 1 minute or until blended. Spread evenly in a 9- by 13-inch cake pan that has been greased with margarine. Bake for 25–30 minutes or until it is browned and starts to pull away from the sides of the pan. Cut into 15 squares and serve warm or at room temperature.

*Yield: 15 servings*

| Nutritive values per serving: | | CHO | PRO | FAT |
|---|---|---|---|---|
| | CAL | (gm) | (gm) | (gm) |
| | 136 | 13 | 3 | 8 |

Food exchanges per serving:          1 BREAD, 1½ FAT

# Carrot Snack Cake

*This recipe has lots of good nutrition and is much lower in fats and sugar than any commercial carrot cake you can buy.*

　　2  cups whole wheat pastry flour
　　1  cup unbleached white flour
　　2  teaspoons baking soda
　　1  teaspoon double-acting baking powder
　　8  ounces nonfat yogurt
　　1  cup finely grated carrots
　　½  cup honey
　　½  cup raisins
　　⅓  cup unsweetened crushed pineapple, drained
　　2  eggs
　　⅓  cup vegetable oil
　　2  tablespoons sesame seeds

1. Preheat oven to 350°F.
2. Combine flours, soda, and baking powder in mixing bowl. Stir well to blend ingredients.
3. Add remaining ingredients except sesame seeds. Beat only to moisten.
4. Spread batter in greased 9- by 13-inch baking pan. Sprinkle on sesame seeds. Bake for about 30 minutes. Cool. Cut into 24 squares.

*Yield: 24 squares*

| Nutritive values per 1-square serving: | | CHO | PRO | FAT |
|---|---|---|---|---|
| | CAL | (gm) | (gm) | (gm) |
| | 124 | 19 | 3 | 4 |

Food exchanges per 1-square
serving:          1 BREAD, ½ FRUIT, 1 FAT

# Vanilla Cheesecake

1½ envelopes unflavored gelatin
½ cup cold water
1 cup evaporated skim milk
1½ cups low-fat vanilla yogurt
2 cups low-fat cottage cheese
1 teaspoon vanilla extract
12 packets artificial sweetener (Equal)
¼ cup diet margarine, melted
¾ cup graham cracker crumbs

1. In a small saucepan, dissolve gelatin in ½ cup cold water and the evaporated milk. Heat mixture until tiny bubbles form around edge of pan. Stir to dissolve gelatin completely. Let cool to room temperature.
2. Using a blender or food processor, combine yogurt and cottage cheese until smooth. (If using a blender, add yogurt first.)
3. Combine yogurt mixture with the cooled milk. Add vanilla extract and sweetener.
4. Refrigerate filling, stirring occasionally, until thickened.
5. Combine margarine and graham cracker crumbs. Mix well. Press mixture evenly on the bottom of a 9-inch springform pan. Bake 8 minutes at 375°F. Cool on a wire rack.
6. Pour filling into crust, cover, and refrigerate at least 4 hours or until firm.

**Variations**

1. To reduce the exchanges for a snack, serve half a slice and top it with ⅓ cup strawberries. (Add ½ FRUIT.)
2. Top the whole cheesecake with 1½ cups sliced strawberries *or* 1 8-ounce can unsweetened crushed pineapple, drained. (Add 10 calories and ¼ FRUIT per serving.)
3. Top each full-slice serving with ½ cup Strawberry Sauce (see index for recipe).

*Yield: 8 servings*

| Nutritive values per serving: | CAL | CHO (gm) | PRO (gm) | FAT (gm) |
|---|---|---|---|---|
| | 247 | 25 | 12 | 11 |

Food exchanges per serving:    ½ BREAD, 1 MILK, 2 FAT

# Oatmeal Bread

*I love homemade bread, and this one is so good that one loaf lasts only about eight hours at my house. If your family likes this bread as much as mine does, you might want to double the recipe. The rising time makes this a little time-consuming, so if you don't work at home, try making it on a weekend. Red-Star makes a "quick-rise" yeast that will rise up to 50 percent faster. Follow the package instructions.*

> 1  cup plus 2 tablespoons skim milk
> 2  tablespoons diet margarine
> 2½ tablespoons honey
> 1¼ teaspoons salt
> 1  package (1 scant tablespoon) active dry yeast
> ¼  cup warm water (105–115°F)
> 1  cup rolled oats (regular or quick, not instant)
> 3–3¼ cups unbleached white flour
>     Vegetable oil

1. Scald milk and add margarine, honey, and salt, stirring until margarine melts. Let mixture cool to between 105 and 115°F.
2. Combine yeast and warm water in a large bowl; let stand 5 minutes. Add milk mixture, oats, and 2 cups flour; mix well. Stir in enough of the remaining flour to make a soft dough.
3. Turn dough out onto a lightly floured surface; knead until smooth and elastic (about 8–10 minutes). Place dough in a large bowl, coated with a little vegetable oil, turning to grease top. Cover and let rise in a warm place (85°F), free from drafts, 1 hour or until doubled in bulk. Punch dough down, cover, and let dough stand 10 minutes.
4. Turn dough out onto a lightly floured surface. Roll into a 15- by 19-inch rectangle. Roll up, jelly roll fashion, beginning at narrow edge. Pinch seam and ends to-

gether to seal; place roll, seam side down, in a 9- by 5-
by 3-inch loaf pan coated with a little vegetable oil.
5. Cover and let rise 50 minutes or until doubled in bulk.
Bake at 375°F for 40–45 minutes. Remove from pan;
cool on wire rack.

**Variation**
Add ½ cup currants, soaked in warm water to plump and
drained, at the end of step 2.

*Yield: 1 loaf*

| Nutritive values per ½-inch-slice serving: | CAL | CHO (gm) | PRO (gm) | FAT (gm) |
|---|---|---|---|---|
| | 110 | 20 | 3 | 2 |

| Food exchanges per ½-inch-slice serving: | 1 BREAD, ½ FRUIT, ½ FAT | | | |
|---|---|---|---|---|

| Nutritive values of variation per ½-inch-slice serving: | CAL | CHO (gm) | PRO (gm) | FAT (gm) |
|---|---|---|---|---|
| | 118 | 22 | 3 | 2 |

| Food exchanges of variation per ½-inch-slice serving: | 1 BREAD, ½ FRUIT, ½ FAT | | | |
|---|---|---|---|---|

# Zucchini Bread

*This recipe is from* The New Diabetic Cookbook, *by Mabel Cavaiani (Contemporary Books, 1984). I use whole wheat pastry flour for added nutrition and fiber.*

> 1   cup unbleached white flour
> ¾  cup whole wheat pastry flour
> 1½ teaspoons ground cinnamon
> ¼  teaspoon salt
> 1   teaspoon baking soda
> ½  teaspoon double-acting baking powder
> 3   large egg whites
> ⅓  cup vegetable oil
> 1½ teaspoons vanilla extract
> 3   packets artificial sweetener (equal to 2 tablespoons sugar)
> 1½ cups well-packed shredded fresh zucchini

1. Preheat oven to 375°F.
2. Place flour, cinnamon, salt, soda, and baking powder in a mixer bowl and mix at low speed to blend well.
3. Place egg whites, oil, vanilla, and sweetener in a cup and mix well with a fork to blend.
4. Add zucchini to flour mixture along with oil mixture and mix at medium speed until well blended and creamy.
5. Pour into 9- by 5- by 3-inch loaf pan that has been greased with diet margarine. Bake for 45 minutes or until a cake tester comes out clean from the center and the bread pulls away from the side of the pan. Cool in the pan for 10 minutes. Turn out onto a wire rack and cool to room temperature.

*Yield: 18 ½-inch slices*

| Nutritive values per ½-inch-slice serving: | CAL | CHO (gm) | PRO (gm) | FAT (gm) |
|---|---|---|---|---|
| | 84 | 10 | 2 | 4 |

Food exchanges per ½-inch-slice
serving:                                    ⅔ BREAD, 1 FAT

# Dinner

Dinner is traditionally the big family meal in this country. Everyone sits down to a hearty meal of meat and potatoes with a tasty dessert. As we discussed earlier, too much of a good thing is still too much. We've become oversaturated (quite literally) with animal proteins and animal fats. With a diabetic in the family, your attention has turned to low-fat cooking and lower-fat foods, less meat, less sugar, etc., and that's the good side of diabetes.

There is every good reason why your whole family will benefit from your child's diabetic diet. There is no good reason you can't enjoy all the family favorites and create new ones as well. This chapter combines familiar dishes like lasagne, pizza, barbecued chicken, and pot roast with new dishes like Lemon Chicken with Bulgur, Salmon Croquettes, Orange Pork Chops with Rice, and Lean Pastichio. They are all formulated with the diabetic's diet requirements *and* family eating in mind.

Generally, I like to delay desserts to a snack time so that the most nutritious food is served for meals. Even so, I have included a few desserts here, even one that's free food! I've added them as suggestions for several different reasons. Lemon Snow Pudding is free, up to a 2-cup serving! Chocolate Delight is a MILK and could easily replace ½ MILK exchange with dinner. The last few dishes—All-American Cranberry Sauce, Cranberry Relish, etc.—are there for special holiday dinners. If your child is allowed a FRUIT exchange at dinner, there are several recipes in "Snacks" that also count as FRUIT— Frozen Fruit Pops, Orange or Pineapple Sherbert, and Wholesome Brownies.

Once again, don't be limited by the way I've organized the meals. There are many dishes in the "Lunch" chapter that are great for dinner. Use the master list of recipes at the back of the book to design your own menus.

This chapter includes lots of starchy and nonstarchy vegetable dishes with which to tempt your children. The best approach with nutrition in general is to eat a wide variety of foods, so try introducing your family to new taste treats. As I discuss in the introduction to Bulgur Pilaf, try introducing new grain products slowly. Mix them half-and-half with a more familiar grain. Tastes can change, but it takes patience.

Also, instead of concentrating on the vegetables your child doesn't eat, make a list, with your child, of the ones she will eat and serve something each child likes at each meal. For example, my secretary, Judy Garcia, chops up all the salad vegetables and lets each family member choose the contents of his salad bowl—sort of a do-it-yourself salad bar. If some of the more seemingly exotic vegetables like Swiss chard aren't big successes, don't worry. Use the "sneaky vegetable" recipes like Tamale Pie and Vegetable and Meat Loaf.

This chapter begins with salad and pasta main courses. Next there are recipes for poultry, fish, and then meats. Potato, rice, grains, and vegetable dishes follow, and the chapter ends with a few salad dressings, a nonfat gravy, and desserts.

Happy eating!

# DINNER MENU IDEAS

You will need to alter these menus to fit your child's diet plan. (Check the index to locate recipes.)

### MENU 1

1 cup Gloria's Spaghetti Sauce with 2 meatballs or sausage — 3 medium-fat MEAT, 2½ VEGETABLE, 2 FAT

1 cup pasta — 2 BREAD

1-2 cups Vegetable Salad: lettuce, grated carrots, — 1 or 2 VEGETABLE, ½ FAT

cucumbers, sprouts, etc.,
with Creamy Vinaigrette
Continental Green Beans          2 VEGETABLE

**TOTAL:** 2 BREAD, 3 medium-fat MEAT, 5½–6½ VEGETABLE, 2½ FAT

---

## MENU 2

BBQ Chicken                      2 lean MEAT, 1 VEGETABLE,
                                     ½ FAT
Carrot–Acorn Squash              1 BREAD, 1 VEGETABLE
Steamed Broccoli                 1 VEGETABLE
Lemon Snow Pudding               FREE

**TOTAL:** 1 BREAD, 2 lean MEAT, 3 VEGETABLE, ½ FAT

---

## MENU 3

Tamale Pie                       1½ BREAD, 1½ medium-fat MEAT,
                                     ½ FAT
Cauliflower Parmesan             1 VEGETABLE, ½ FAT
Baked Spinach                    1 VEGETABLE, ½ FAT
Apple Salad (from "Snacks"       1 FRUIT
    chapter)

**TOTAL:** 1½ BREAD, 1 FRUIT, 1½ medium-fat MEAT, 2 VEGETABLE,
1½ FAT

---

## MENU 4

Lemon Chicken                    3 lean MEAT, ½ FAT
Corn Pudding                     1 BREAD, ½ MILK, ½ lean MEAT,
                                     1 FAT
Salad with Tangy Buttermilk      2 VEGETABLE
    Dressing
Zucchini Italiano                2 VEGETABLE ·
Chocolate Delight                ½ MILK, trace FAT

**TOTAL:** 1 BREAD, 1 MILK, 3½ lean MEAT, 4 VEGETABLE, 1½ FAT

---

## MENU 5

Chicken & Vegetable Stir-Fry     3½ lean MEAT, 2 VEGETABLE
1 cup rice                       2 BREAD
Cucumber Salad                   ½ VEGETABLE, trace FAT
Pineapple Sherbert (from         ½ FRUIT
    "Snacks" chapter)

**TOTAL:** 2 BREAD, ½ FRUIT, 3½ lean MEAT, 2½ VEGETABLE, trace
FAT

# DINNER EXCHANGES

Use this list as a quick reference when planning dinner menus. A glance at the right-hand column should give you ideas of what to serve for certain exchanges called for in your child's diet plan. The recipes are listed here in the same order as they appear in the chapter.

| | |
|---|---|
| Linguine with Red Clam Sauce | 2 BREAD, 3 lean MEAT, 1 VEGETABLE |
| Lasagne with Meat and Vegetables | 1½ BREAD, 3 medium-fat MEAT, 2 VEGETABLE, 1½ FAT |
| Spinach Manicotti | 2 BREAD, 1½ medium-fat MEAT, 3 VEGETABLE |
| Pasta with Tuna and Tomato Sauce | 2 BREAD, 2 lean MEAT, 1 VEGETABLE |
| Whole Wheat Pizza | 2 BREAD, 3 medium-fat MEAT, 1 VEGETABLE |
| Tamale Pie | 1½ BREAD, 1½ medium-fat MEAT, ½ FAT |
| Gloria's Spaghetti Sauce With Meat | 2½ VEGETABLE, trace FAT 3 medium-fat MEAT, 2½ VEGETABLE, 2 FAT |
| Fast Spaghetti Sauce | 1½ medium-fat MEAT, 2 VEGETABLE |
| With Spaghetti Squash | 1 BREAD |
| Chinese Chicken Salad | 1½ lean MEAT, 2 VEGETABLE, 2 FAT |
| Taco Salad | 1 BREAD, 1½ high-fat MEAT, 2 VEGETABLE |
| Lemon Chicken | 3 lean MEAT, ½ FAT |
| Chicken and Vegetable Stir-Fry | 3½ lean MEAT, 2 VEGETABLE |
| Chicken Cacciatore | 3 lean MEAT, 2 VEGETABLE, ½ FAT |
| Lemon Chicken with Bulgur | 3 BREAD, 3 medium-fat MEAT |
| Foiled Chicken | 3 lean MEAT, 1 VEGETABLE |
| Orange Chicken | 3 lean MEAT |

| | |
|---|---|
| BBQ Chicken | 2 lean MEAT, 1 VEGETABLE, ½ FAT |
| Oven-Fried Chicken | 2 BREAD, 3½ lean MEAT, trace FAT |
| Peanut Butter Chicken | 2 lean MEAT, 1½ VEGETABLE, 1 FAT |
| Chicken Pizzaiola | 1½ BREAD, 4½ lean MEAT, 3 VEGETABLE, 1½ FAT |
| Chicken Cordon Bleu | ⅓ BREAD, 4 lean MEAT, ½ FAT |
| Brunswick Stew | 2 BREAD, 2½ lean MEAT |
| Turkey Loaf | 3 lean MEAT, 1½ VEGETABLE |
| Roast Stuffed Turkey | 5 lean MEAT |
| Stuffing with Whole Wheat Bread | 1⅔ BREAD |
| With ½ Bread and ½ Cornbread | 2 BREAD, trace FAT |
| With Cornbread | 2 BREAD, ½ FAT |
| Turkey Burgers | ⅓ BREAD, 2 lean MEAT |
| Turkey Tetrazzini | 2 BREAD, 2 lean MEAT, trace FAT |
| Seafood Stew | 5½ lean MEAT, 1 VEGETABLE |
| Oven "French-Fried" Scallops | ⅔ BREAD, 3 lean MEAT |
| Saucy Scallops | ½ BREAD, 4 lean MEAT |
| Foiled Fish Fillets | 4½ lean MEAT |
| Oven Fish Fillets | ⅓ MILK, 3 lean MEAT |
| Salmon Croquettes | 1 BREAD, 3 lean MEAT |
| Mustard Sauce | ½ FAT |
| Lean Pastichio | 1 BREAD, 2 medium-fat MEAT, 1 VEGETABLE |
| With Feta Cheese | 1 BREAD, 2½ medium-fat MEAT, 1 VEGETABLE |
| Beef and Tomato Stir-Fry | 1 BREAD, 3 lean MEAT, 2 VEGETABLE |
| Oriental Flank Steak | 4 lean MEAT, ½ FAT |
| Pot Roast | 1 BREAD, 4½ medium-fat MEAT |
| Beef and Snow Peas | 2 lean MEAT, 1½ VEGETABLE, ½ FAT |

| | |
|---|---|
| Vegetable and Meat Loaf | 3 lean MEAT, 1 VEGETABLE |
| Swiss Steak | ½ BREAD, 4 lean MEAT, 1 VEGETABLE, ½ FAT |
| Superb Oven Stew | 2 BREAD, 4 lean MEAT |
| Veal Scaloppine | ⅓ BREAD, 3 lean MEAT, ½ FAT |
| Osso Buco | 3 lean MEAT, 1 VEGETABLE |
| Veal Chops with Raspberry Vinegar | 3 lean MEAT, ½ FAT |
| Greek Lamb Chops | 3 lean MEAT |
| Lovely Lamb Stew | 1 BREAD, 4 lean MEAT |
| Baked Lamb Chops | 1 FRUIT, 3 lean MEAT, ½ FAT |
| Orange Pork Chops with Rice | 1½ BREAD, 1 FRUIT, 4 lean MEAT |
| Noodle Kugel | 2 BREAD, 1 FRUIT, 1 lean MEAT |
| Red Beans and Rice | 3 BREAD, 1 lean MEAT, 1 VEGETABLE |
| Rice and Vegetable Casserole | 1 BREAD, 1½ VEGETABLE |
| Bulgur Pilaf | 2 BREAD |
| Oven "French Fries" | 1 BREAD, ½ FAT |
| Potato-Bean Patties | 1 BREAD, 1 medium-fat MEAT |
| Potato Kugel | 1 BREAD, trace FAT |
| Stuffed Yams | 2 BREAD, ½ FRUIT |
| Puffed Sweet Potatoes | 2 BREAD |
| Sweet Potatoes and Bananas | 1 BREAD, 1 FRUIT |
| Carrot–Acorn Squash | 1 BREAD, 1 VEGETABLE |
| Corn Pudding | 1 BREAD, ½ MILK, ½ lean MEAT, 1 FAT |
| Squash with Apples | 1 BREAD, 1 FRUIT, trace FAT |
| Oven-Fried Squash | ½ BREAD, 1 VEGETABLE, trace FAT |
| Cauliflower or Broccoli Parmesan | 1 VEGETABLE, ½ FAT |
| Sesame Broccoli Variation | 1½ VEGETABLE, ½ FAT 2½ VEGETABLE, ½ FAT |

| | |
|---|---|
| Tart Red Cabbage | 1 FRUIT, 1 VEGETABLE |
| Sautéed Cabbage | 1 VEGETABLE |
| Fruit Spiced Carrots | 1 VEGETABLE |
| Cucumber Salad | ½ VEGETABLE, trace FAT |
| Continental Green Beans | 2 VEGETABLE |
| Baked Spinach | 1 VEGETABLE, ½ FAT |
| Stir-Fry Squash | 1 VEGETABLE, ½ FAT |
| Zucchini Italiano | 2 VEGETABLE |
| Swiss Chard Sauté | 1½ VEGETABLE, ½ FAT |
| Mashed Turnips | 1½ VEGETABLE |
| Hash Brown Turnips | 1½ VEGETABLE |
| Chinese Vegetables | 1½ VEGETABLE |
| Skillet Vegetables | ½ high-fat MEAT, 2 VEGETABLE |
| Popovers | 1 BREAD, 1 FAT |
| No-Calorie Dressing | FREE up to ½ cup |
| Tangy Buttermilk Dressing | FREE up to ⅓ cup |
| Mock Thousand Island Dressing | ½ BREAD |
| Creamy Vinaigrette | ½ FAT |
| Low-Calorie Mayonnaise | ½ lean MEAT, ½ FAT |
| Gravy from Meat Drippings | FREE |
| Lemon Snow Pudding | FREE up to 2 cups |
| Chocolate Delight | ½ MILK, trace FAT |
| Chocolate Sauce | ¼ MILK, trace FAT |
| All-American Cranberry Sauce | ½ FRUIT |
| Cranberry Relish | ½ FRUIT; up to 4 tablespoons FREE |
| Cranberry Mold | 1 FRUIT, ½ FAT |
| Cran-Apple Crisp | ½ BREAD, 1½ FRUIT, 1 FAT |
| Easy Sugarless Pumpkin Pie | 1½ BREAD, ½ MILK, 1 FAT |

# Recipes

## PASTA PLUS

Most of us have had the mistaken notion that pasta is a fattening filler food, laden with calories and not terribly nutritious. Nothing could be further from the truth. Pasta is a nourishing food that fills you up before you eat more calories than you need. Pasta is also an ideal basic food for diabetics since it is very low on the glycemic index; therefore, it does not cause blood sugar to rise very much after a meal.

A 1-cup serving of cooked pasta weighs about 5 ounces, has only 200 calories, and has half the calories of a steak the same size. The 1-cup serving counts as 2 BREAD. The problem with pasta is that we Americans tend to drown it in rich cream and butter-laden sauces. Even ⅔ cup plain canned tomato sauce counts as 1 BREAD. The secret is to keep the fat content very low and add fiber to the sauces. I use canned whole tomatoes and puree them very briefly, leaving chunks of tomato still intact. Better yet, break up the tomatoes by hand. Sneaky vegetables—chopped onion, spinach, broccoli, and grated carrots—add important fiber to the sauce.

If your child loves pasta but is allowed only 2 BREAD at dinner, try trading the carbohydrates from another exchange like FRUIT or MILK. The 10 grams of carbohydrate in a FRUIT would count as ⅔ BREAD, hence another ⅓ cup pasta. A MILK is 12 grams, which would be almost the same as 1 BREAD (15 grams carbohydrate), allowing another ½-cup serving. I discuss trading exchanges in detail in Part III: "The Copebook."

You do not need to add salt to the water in which you cook your pasta. If no salt is added, a 1-cup serving of pasta contains less than 10 milligrams of sodium. Pasta also contains reasonable amounts of thiamine, riboflavin, niacin, and iron and 5 grams of protein per 1-cup serving.

Pasta comes dried or fresh, in many colors, in dozens of different shapes and sizes, and from many different types of flour. Pasta from durum wheat semolina cooks up firm and slightly chewy (al dente—"to the tooth") if not over-cooked. There are new high-protein pastas available. They contain approximately 13 grams of protein per 1-cup serving, the same amount you would get from 2 ounces of meat. Pastas are a good idea for children who are fussy eaters. I've never met a child who didn't like pasta. You can serve it with a tomato sauce with sneaky vegetables (Gloria's Spaghetti Sauce) or plain with a glass of milk and carrot sticks, for instance, and know your child has had a nutritious meal.

Whole wheat pasta is available in health food stores and some large supermarkets. It has more fiber, vitamins, and minerals than regular pasta, but the taste and texture are much different. Try mixing the two, but cook them sepa-rately. Whole wheat pasta can get mushy if cooked as long as regular pasta.

You can now buy fresh pasta—pasta that has not been dried. You don't necessarily get a superior product, al-though you'll pay a premium price. Also, fresh pasta contains more water than dried, so the price per pound cannot be compared directly. A pound of fresh pasta does not go as far as a pound of dried. Fresh pasta absorbs sauce more readily, so it works best with light sauces. It cooks very quickly—in 2–6 minutes as compared to 8–20 minutes for dried pasta.

Cook pasta in a large pot with 4–6 quarts of water per pound of pasta. The more water, the less gummy the pasta will be. Add the pasta to the rapidly boiling water in batches over a span of no more than 1 minute. Drain in a colander and do not rinse it unless it's to be used for a cold salad.

# Linguine with Red Clam Sauce

*If your child likes clams still in their shells, use fresh clams. If not, use canned clams. I first had this years ago in Italy, prepared by the waiter at the table after I told him I love clams.*

1 clove garlic, minced or pressed
1 tablespoon extra-virgin olive oil
¼ cup white wine
1 16-ounce can tomatoes
2 tablespoons tomato paste
1 teaspoon basil leaves
½ teaspoon oregano leaves
2 tablespoons chopped fresh parsley
¼ teaspoon freshly ground pepper
Juice of ½ lemon
1 dozen Little Neck clams *or* 2 10-ounce cans clams, whole or chopped
8 ounces dry linguine, cooked al dente

1. In large skillet, sauté garlic in oil over medium heat until softened, 2 or 3 minutes. Do not let it brown.
2. Add remaining ingredients except clams and linguine and simmer over low heat for 20–25 minutes. Stir and break up tomatoes.
3. Add clams, whole in shells or canned (with juice). Cover and steam whole clams for 10 minutes or until clams open or for 3 or 4 minutes if using canned clams.
4. Toss with hot, drained pasta and serve.

*Yield: 4 1½-cup servings*

| Nutritive values per 1½-cup serving: | CAL | CHO (gm) | PRO (gm) | FAT (gm) |
|---|---|---|---|---|
| | 289 | 35 | 26 | 5 |

Food exchanges per 1½-cup
serving:                        2 BREAD, 3 lean MEAT,
                                1 VEGETABLE

# Lasagne with Meat and Vegetables

½ pound lean ground beef
4 sweet Italian sausages, removed from casings (about ½ pound)
1 bunch spinach (approximately 1 pound)
1 large stalk broccoli (about ½ pound)
¼ cup water
½ recipe Gloria's Spaghetti Sauce without meat (about 6 cups) (see index for recipe)
8 ounces lasagne noodles
1 cup low-fat cottage cheese
1 cup ricotta cheese
2 eggs, beaten
¼ cup Parmesan cheese
¼ cup minced fresh parsley
1 cup shredded part-skim mozzarella cheese

1. Preheat oven to 375°F.
2. Fry beef and sausage in large skillet over medium heat until well browned but still soft. Drain well on paper towels in a colander. Wipe all drippings from pan.
3. Clean spinach, remove stems, and shred spinach with a sharp knife, cutting across the leaf. Cut tough ends off the bottom of the broccoli. Peel the stems. Chop the flowerets and stems. Put the spinach and broccoli in skillet, add ¼ cup water, cover, and steam over medium heat for 5 minutes.
4. Add the meat and vegetables to the sauce and simmer for 30–45 minutes.
5. Meanwhile, cook the lasagne noodles a few at a time in lots of boiling water until al dente. Drain and spread on wax paper.
6. Combine the cottage cheese, ricotta, eggs, Parmesan cheese, and parsley.
7. When sauce is ready, spread ½ cup sauce in the bottom of a 13- by 9-inch baking dish. Next, put in a layer of noodles, ½ the cottage cheese mixture, ½ the mozzarella, 1 cup sauce, another layer of noodles, the remain-

ing cottage cheese mixture, 1 cup sauce, remaining noodles, 1 cup sauce, and the remaining mozzarella. Reserve extra sauce to pass separately.

**8.** Bake for 30–40 minutes until cheese is bubbling. Remove from oven and allow to stand 20 minutes before cutting. Cut into 10 equal portions.

*Yield: 10 1½-cup servings*

| Nutritive values per 1½-cup serving: | CAL | CHO (gm) | PRO (gm) | FAT (gm) |
|---|---|---|---|---|
| | 423 | 26 | 28 | 23 |

Food exchanges per 1½-cup serving:

1½ BREAD, 3 medium-fat MEAT, 1 VEGETABLE, 1½ FAT

# Spinach Manicotti

*I've found the easiest way to stuff the shells is to use a pastry bag with a wide tip. If you don't have a pastry bag, slit one side of each shell with a sharp knife, open it, and fill. Place the cut side down in the baking dish and no one will be the wiser! If you use a spaghetti sauce from a jar, look for one with no added sugar.*

    10  manicotti shells
     2  10-ounce packages frozen chopped spinach
        *or* 2 bunches (approximately 1 pound each) fresh
     1  16-ounce carton low-fat cottage cheese, drained, *or* 1 16-ounce carton ricotta cheese
    ⅓  cup grated Parmesan cheese
    ¼  teaspoon ground nutmeg
        Freshly ground pepper, to taste
    ¼  teaspoon extra-virgin olive oil
     4  cups meatless spaghetti sauce (preferably homemade)
    ¼  cup chopped fresh parsley

**1.** Preheat oven to 350°F.
**2.** Cook manicotti shells according to package directions, omitting salt; drain and set aside.
**3.** Cook spinach according to package directions, omitting salt. Drain, place on paper towels, and squeeze until barely moist. Or wash fresh spinach, remove stems, and shred across leaf. Steam for 5 minutes and drain thoroughly.
**4.** Combine spinach, cottage cheese, Parmesan cheese, nutmeg, and pepper. Stuff manicotti shells with spinach mixture and arrange in a 13- by 9-inch baking dish wiped with olive oil.
**5.** Pour spaghetti sauce over manicotti. Bake for 45 minutes. Sprinkle with parsley.

*Yield: 5 servings (2 manicotti each)*

| Nutritive values per serving: | CAL | CHO (gm) | PRO (gm) | FAT (gm) |
|---|---|---|---|---|
| | 350 | 44 | 21 | 10 |

Food exchanges per serving:  2 BREAD, 1½ medium-fat
MEAT, 3 VEGETABLE

# Pasta with Tuna and Tomato Sauce

*I tasted this in Italy, where it was called Spaghetti with Tuna Sauce, and it was delicious. This is my adaptation of it.*

2   cloves garlic, minced or pressed
1   tablespoon extra-virgin olive oil
1   anchovy fillet
½   medium onion, chopped
1   16-ounce can Italian tomatoes, pureed in blender briefly
1   teaspoon basil leaves
¼   teaspoon ground allspice
¼   teaspoon freshly ground pepper
1   7-ounce can tuna packed in water, drained and flaked
¼   cup minced fresh parsley
8   ounces dry pasta, such as rigatoni or rotini (corkscrews) or shells, cooked al dente

1. In large skillet, sauté garlic in oil. Mash anchovy and stir in. Cook for 1 minute.
2. Add onion, tomatoes, and seasonings. Heat to boiling, reduce heat, and simmer for 20 minutes, covered.
3. Add tuna and parsley. Simmer for 10 minutes more.
4. Toss with hot, drained pasta and serve.

*Yield: 4 1½-cup servings*

| Nutritive values per 1½-cup serving: | CAL | CHO (gm) | PRO (gm) | FAT (gm) |
|---|---|---|---|---|
| | 269 | 35 | 21 | 5 |

Food exchanges per 1½-cup serving:  2 BREAD, 2 lean MEAT,
1 VEGETABLE

# Whole Wheat Pizza

*Here's a dinner project in which the whole family can participate. You can use your own homemade sauce or a commercial sauce in a jar. If it's not thick, simmer it for 20–25 minutes to reduce and thicken. Measure after reducing.*

½ cup warm water (105–115°F)
1 tablespoon extra-virgin olive oil
1 teaspoon sugar
½ teaspoon salt
½ package (about 1 teaspoon) dry yeast
¾ cup unbleached white flour
¾ cup whole wheat flour
Olive oil
½ pound lean ground beef
1 cup thick tomato sauce (preferably homemade or low-sodium)
1 cup (4 ounces) shredded mozzarella cheese
2 tablespoons grated Parmesan cheese
Crushed hot red pepper (optional)

1. Combine water, 1 tablespoon olive oil, sugar, and salt in a medium mixing bowl. Sprinkle yeast over mixture, stirring until dissolved. Gradually add flours, mixing well after each addition.
2. Turn dough out onto a lightly floured surface and knead about 4 minutes or until smooth and elastic. Shape into a ball and place in a bowl coated with a little olive oil, turning to grease top. Cover and let rise in a warm place (85°F), free from drafts, 1 hour or until doubled in bulk.
3. Coat a 12-inch pizza pan with ½ teaspoon olive oil and set aside. Punch dough down. Lightly coat hands with oil and pat dough evenly into pizza pan. Bake at 425°F for 5 minutes.
4. Cook ground beef in a skillet over medium heat until meat is browned, stirring to crumble. Drain well on paper towels.

**5.** Spread 1 cup tomato sauce evenly over pizza crust, leaving a ½-inch border around edges. Sprinkle mozzarella cheese over top. Sprinkle meat over mozzarella, then sprinkle on Parmesan cheese and red pepper flakes. Bake at 425°F 15 minutes, until cheese is bubbling.

*Yield: 1 large pizza (4 servings, 2 wedges each)*

| Nutritive values per 2-wedge serving: | CAL | CHO (gm) | PRO (gm) | FAT (gm) |
|---|---|---|---|---|
| | 397 | 36 | 25 | 17 |

Food exchanges per 2-wedge serving: 2 BREAD, 3 medium-fat MEAT, 1 VEGETABLE

# Tamale Pie

*This should be subtitled "with more sneaky vegetables."
Using less meat and more vegetables is a great way to
increase fiber and lower fat. Cook the pinto or red beans
fresh. It doesn't take that long. Cover them with water
and simmer for 1½–2 hours. You can use canned if you
must. Brennan loved this, and Robin didn't. You can't
win 'em all!*

### Filling
1 pound lean ground beef
2 tablespoons chopped capers
2 cloves garlic, minced or pressed
1 medium onion, chopped
2 medium green peppers, chopped fine
1 tablespoon extra-virgin olive oil
2 tablespoons tomato paste
1 teaspoon ground cumin
2 tablespoons chili powder
½ cup water
3 cups cooked pinto or red beans (1½ cups dried before cooking) *or* 1½ 16-ounce cans, drained and rinsed
1 cup fresh or frozen corn kernels
¼ cup sliced green olives
¼ cup minced fresh parsley

### Crust
1 cup stone-ground yellow cornmeal
2 tablespoons unbleached white flour
1½ teaspoons baking powder
1 egg, beaten
½ cup skim milk
1 tablespoon vegetable oil
¼ cup grated sharp Cheddar cheese

**1.** Preheat oven to 375°F.
**2.** Sauté beef in large skillet until browned, stirring as it cooks to break up meat. Drain meat thoroughly and spread in the bottom of a 2-quart casserole.

3. In the same skillet, sauté capers, garlic, onion, and peppers in olive oil until softened, 5 minutes or so, over medium heat.

4. Stir in tomato paste, cumin, chili powder, water, beans, corn, olives, and parsley. Stir to combine and cook until mixture is heated through, 10 minutes or so. Pour this mixture on top of meat in casserole and spread evenly.

5. In medium bowl, combine cornmeal, flour, baking powder, egg, milk, and vegetable oil. Spread on top of bean mixture and top with grated cheese.

6. Bake for 25–30 minutes, until bubbly hot and dough is golden brown.

*Yield: 10 1-cup servings*

| Nutritive values per 1-cup serving: | CAL | CHO (gm) | PRO (gm) | FAT (gm) |
|---|---|---|---|---|
| | 239 | 22 | 13 | 11 |

Food exchanges per 1-cup serving:

1½ BREAD, 1½ medium-fat MEAT, ½ FAT

## PASTA SAUCES

# Gloria's Spaghetti Sauce (Meatless or with Meat)

*My dad is a very good cook, and he taught me to respect well-spiced food. This is an adaptation of his recipe, and I always get compliments on it. The addition of aniseed (tastes like licorice) is the secret.*

1 tablespoon olive oil
3 cloves garlic, minced very fine
1 large onion, chopped fine
3 carrots, shredded
1/4 pound fresh mushrooms, chopped (optional)
1/2 cup chopped fresh parsley
2 tablespoons basil leaves
1/2 teaspoon oregano leaves
1 tablespoon aniseed, crushed (use 2 tablespoons if no meat is used)
1 1/2 cups or more dry red wine (Burgundy or Chianti)
2 28-ounce cans whole tomatoes
1 12-ounce can tomato paste

1. Heat olive oil in heavy Dutch oven over medium-low heat. Add garlic and sauté for a few minutes—don't let it brown. Add onion, carrots, mushrooms, parsley, basil, oregano, aniseed, and red wine. Simmer for 10 minutes.
2. Meanwhile, run the tomatoes through a blender or food processor, then add to skillet along with the tomato paste.
3. Cover and let simmer 3–4 hours. Stir several times each hour. Add more wine if too thick.

*Yield: 12 cups*

| Nutritive values per 1-cup serving: | CAL | CHO (gm) | PRO (gm) | FAT (gm) |
|---|---|---|---|---|
| | 69 | 12 | 3 | 1 |

Food exchanges per 1-cup
serving:                        2½ VEGETABLE, trace FAT

(It can be counted as VEGETABLE *or* BREAD. It may affect the blood sugar like a BREAD.)

**Variation**

*To make meat sauce, use the same ingredients and directions above, but use only 1 tablespoon aniseed.*

8   sweet Italian sausages (approximately 1 pound)
2   pounds lean ground beef
¼   cup wheat germ
¼   cup Parmesan cheese
1   egg
2   tablespoons Worcestershire sauce
    Freshly ground pepper
½   teaspoon oregano leaves

1. Cut each Italian sausage into 4 pieces and brown in heavy skillet. Drain well on paper towels to cut down on grease. Wipe out skillet.
2. Mix remaining ingredients into meatballs the same size as sausage pieces (approximately 1 inch in diameter) and brown in skillet. Drain well.
3. Add sausages and meatballs to sauce after first hour of simmering.

*Yield: 12 cups*

| Nutritive values per 1-cup serving: | CAL | CHO (gm) | PRO (gm) | FAT (gm) |
|---|---|---|---|---|
| | 386 | 13 | 25 | 26 |

Food exchanges per 1-cup
serving:                        3 medium-fat MEAT,
                                2½ VEGETABLE, 2 FAT *or*
                                ⅔ BREAD, 3 medium-fat MEAT,
                                2 FAT

# Fast Spaghetti Sauce with Spaghetti Squash

*Here's a quick sauce to make in the microwave. The spaghetti squash is very much like spaghetti, and it has fewer calories plus good fiber. Toss the squash strands with a little sauce before serving and pass extra sauce separately. This makes a very low-calorie, filling main dish when served with Spaghetti Squash. You might also make some pasta the first time, in case the newness of the squash doesn't enjoy instant success with all your family members!*

1 pound lean ground beef
1 medium onion, chopped
½ cup chopped celery
¾ cup chopped green pepper
2 carrots, grated
¼ cup chopped fresh parsley
1 clove garlic, minced or pressed
1 teaspoon oregano leaves
1 teaspoon basil leaves
1 tablespoon aniseed, crushed
2 16-ounce cans whole tomatoes, pureed
1 6-ounce can tomato paste
¼ cup red wine

1. Place ground beef in a hard plastic colander. Place vegetables through garlic on top of meat. Place colander over a casserole dish.
2. Microwave on high for 6 minutes, stirring after 3 minutes. Discard any fat that cooks out.
3. Add remaining ingredients to meat and vegetables, place in a 3-quart casserole, and mix well.
4. Cook on high for 10 minutes. Stir and continue cooking 30–35 minutes on simmer.
5. Serve with Spaghetti Squash (see following recipe) or pasta.

*Yield: 8 1-cup servings*

| Nutritive values per 1-cup serving: | CAL | CHO (gm) | PRO (gm) | FAT (gm) |
|---|---|---|---|---|
|  | 156 | 9 | 12 | 8 |

Food exchanges per 1-cup
serving:                                        1 BREAD, 1½ medium-fat
                                                MEAT, 2 VEGETABLE

# Spaghetti Squash

1 large spaghetti squash (approximately
   5½–6 pounds)

1. Pierce the squash with a knife and place on a paper towel.
2. Cook in microwave on high for 15 minutes. Turn about 4 times while it is cooking. Or you can cut it in half lengthwise, remove seeds, place cut sides down on a baking sheet, and bake for 30–40 minutes, until tender, at 350°F. When done, knife should insert easily.
3. Let it stand 3 minutes after cooking.
4. Cut in half, remove seeds, and pull the strands free with two serving forks.

**Variation**
If desired, toss squash strands with 2 tablespoons diet margarine (add 1 FAT per serving).

*Yield: Approximately 5–6 servings*

| Nutritive values per 1-cup serving: | CAL | CHO (gm) | PRO (gm) | FAT (gm) |
|---|---|---|---|---|
|  | 68 | 15 | 2 | 0 |

Food exchanges per 1-cup
serving:                                        1 BREAD

# MAIN COURSE SALADS

## Chinese Chicken Salad

*My mom also gave me this recipe. It takes a bit of work, but it's worth it. The hoisin sauce is available in Oriental markets and some supermarkets. Most large supermarkets carry the dark sesame oil and rice vinegar. If not, you can get it at an Oriental market. It adds a very special flavor!*

- 2 chicken breast halves, skinned
  Water or stock
- 2 green onions, cut up
- 2 slices peeled fresh gingerroot
- 2 teaspoons dark sesame oil
- 1 slice peeled fresh gingerroot, minced
- 2 tablespoons hoisin sauce
- 2 tablespoons rice vinegar
- 1 small head iceberg lettuce, shredded
- 2 tablespoons minced fresh parsley or cilantro
- 2 green onions, cut into 2-inch lengths and shredded
- 2 tablespoons sesame seeds
- ¼ pound Chinese pea pods, cut julienne or into diagonal strips
- 1 tablespoon peanut oil
- 1 teaspoon dark sesame oil
- 1 tablespoon soy sauce

1. Poach chicken breasts in water or stock to cover with 2 green onions and 2 ginger slices. Bring to a simmer over medium heat, lower heat, and simmer for 10 minutes. Turn breasts over and let stand 15 minutes.
2. When chicken is cooled, heat 2 teaspoons sesame oil in wok or large skillet over medium-high heat. When hot, add minced ginger. Cook until browned, a few minutes, then remove ginger and discard.
3. Shred chicken into long thin strands and add it to oil

in wok. Stir over medium-high heat for 1 or 2 minutes. Add hoisin sauce and vinegar. Remove from heat.

4. Combine lettuce, parsley or cilantro, 2 green onions, sesame seeds, and pea pods. Toss and add shredded chicken. Add peanut oil, 1 teaspoon sesame oil, and soy sauce. Toss to mix well. Serve immediately.

*Yield: 4 1½-cup servings*

| Nutritive values per 1½-cup serving: | CAL | CHO (gm) | PRO (gm) | FAT (gm) |
|---|---|---|---|---|
| | 231 | 9 | 15 | 15 |

| Food exchanges per 1½-cup serving: | 1½ lean MEAT, 2 VEGETABLE, 2 FAT |
|---|---|

# Taco Salad

*Taco Salad, like Chinese Chicken Salad (recipe follows), is a good one-dish meal (if your kids eat salad!). If you like a little more moisture, try a little extra sprinkling of lemon juice or wine vinegar.*

1 cup low-calorie Italian dressing
1 tablespoon chili powder
1 teaspoon ground cumin
1 pound lean ground beef, browned, drained, and cooled
2 cups cooked pinto beans
2 tomatoes, chopped
1 small head lettuce, shredded
4 green onions, chopped
1 green pepper, chopped
1 cup chopped Homemade Tortilla Chips (see index) or commercial taco chips
1 cup grated Cheddar cheese

1. Mix dressing, chili powder, and cumin with beef.
2. Place all other ingredients in a large bowl. Add beef and toss gently. *Or* layer the ingredients, with lettuce on the bottom, followed by beans, onions, tomatoes, peppers, and meat, and top with chips and cheese.

*Yield: 8 1¼-cup servings*

| Nutritive values per 1½-cup serving: | CAL | CHO (gm) | PRO (gm) | FAT (gm) |
|---|---|---|---|---|
| | 268 | 14 | 17 | 16 |

| Food exchanges per 1½-cup serving: | 1 BREAD, 1½ high-fat MEAT, 2 VEGETABLE |
|---|---|

# POULTRY
## Chicken

I've included lots of chicken recipes. Chicken is versatile, appeals to almost all children and adults, and is a relatively inexpensive animal protein source. All these recipes use skinned chicken, which saves lots of calories and fat per serving.

# Lemon Chicken

*This is always a great success with my boys. They love the lemony flavor. I've marinated this as long as 48 hours because of last-minute changes in dinner plans, and it was even tastier!*

> 4  chicken breast halves, skinned and boned
>    Juice of 2 lemons
> 1  tablespoon unsalted butter
> ½  cup dry white wine

1. Flatten chicken with a tenderizer or mallet to about ¼-inch thickness. Pour lemon juice over and marinate in refrigerator at least 4 hours.
2. Melt butter in a skillet over medium heat. Sauté breasts for 5 minutes on each side. Remove and place on hot platter to keep warm.
3. Pour wine into skillet, stirring. Let boil for a few minutes, then pour over the chicken.

**Variation:**
Add 1 teaspoon ground cumin to the lemon juice.

*Yield: 4 servings*

| Nutritive values per serving: | CAL | CHO (gm) | PRO (gm) | FAT (gm) |
|---|---|---|---|---|
| | 192 | 0 | 21 | 12 |

Food exchanges per serving:      3 lean MEAT, ½ FAT

# Chicken and Vegetable Stir-Fry

*This is quick and easy. You can make the marinade in the morning, put the rice on 30 minutes before dinner, and then cut the vegetables and start cooking.*

2 tablespoons water
3 tablespoons rice vinegar
2 tablespoons soy sauce (preferably reduced-sodium)
1 tablespoon cream sherry
1 clove garlic, minced or pressed
1 thin slice peeled gingerroot, minced, *or*
½ teaspoon dried ginger
2 green onions, with tops, sliced
1 pound boneless chicken breasts, skinned and cut into thin strips
2 teaspoons sesame oil
1 cup celery, sliced diagonally
1 cup carrots, sliced diagonally
1 cup broccoli, flowerets and stems, peeled and sliced
1 cup Chinese pea pods, stem ends snipped
1 tablespoon sesame seeds

**1.** In a glass dish, combine water, vinegar, soy sauce, sherry, garlic, ginger, onions, and chicken and refrigerate for at least 2 hours (the longer, the better).
**2.** Drain chicken and reserve marinade.
**3.** In a large skillet or wok, heat sesame oil over medium-high heat until hot. Add chicken and cook, stirring constantly, until chicken loses its pink color. Remove chicken.
**4.** Add celery, carrots, and broccoli and cook, stirring, for 3 minutes. Add pea pods and marinade and cover. Let vegetables steam for 2–3 minutes.
**5.** Add chicken and sesame seeds and stir to combine. Vegetables should be crisp-tender, pea pods still bright green. Serve with Chinese or Korean rice, if available.

*Yield: 4 1¼-cup servings*

| Nutritive values per 1¼-cup serving: | CAL | CHO (gm) | PRO (gm) | FAT (gm) |
|---|---|---|---|---|
| | 270 | 10 | 26 | 14 |

Food exchanges per 1¼-cup serving:                           3½ lean MEAT, 2 VEGETABLE

# Chicken Cacciatore

*This dish is traditionally made with whole chicken pieces. That adds a lot of fat and is messy to eat. My boys liked this much better with the boneless breasts. The recipe is courtesy of Joe Gallison, the fine actor who played my husband on "Days of Our Lives."*

  6  boneless chicken breast halves, skinned
  1  tablespoon olive oil
  2  cloves garlic, minced
  1  medium onion, chopped
  1  8-ounce can tomato sauce
  2  16-ounce cans tomatoes
  2  teaspoons basil leaves
  1  teaspoon oregano leaves
  1  teaspoon rosemary leaves
  ¼  teaspoon freshly ground pepper
  ¼  cup red wine
  2  green peppers, cut into strips
  ¼  pound fresh mushrooms, sliced

**1.** Sauté breasts in olive oil a few minutes per side in a large skillet over medium heat.
**2.** Add all remaining ingredients to skillet. Break up the tomatoes with a wooden spoon. Cover and simmer for 40 minutes.

*Yield: 6 servings*

| Nutritive values per serving: | CAL | CHO (gm) | PRO (gm) | FAT (gm) |
|---|---|---|---|---|
| | 239 | 11 | 24 | 11 |

Food exchanges per serving:        3 lean MEAT, 2 VEGETABLE, ½ FAT

# Lemon Chicken with Bulgur

*This delicious high-fiber dish is from Jane Brody's Good Food Book. You can make it with kasha (buckwheat groats) instead of bulgur. I also like it with extra lemon or you can serve it with lemon wedges. The servings will include ½ cup bulgur per person.*

> 2 teaspoons butter or margarine
> 2 teaspoons olive or peanut oil
> 1 3½-pound broiler-fryer, skinned and cut into serving pieces
> Salt to taste (optional)
> Freshly ground pepper to taste
> 3 medium onions, chopped (1½–2 cups)
> 2 cloves garlic, minced (2 teaspoons)
> 1½ cups bulgur
> ½ teaspoon ground cardamom
> ½ teaspoon ground coriander
> ½ teaspoon ground cumin
> Grated zest and juice of 1 lemon
> 3 cups boiling chicken broth

**1.** Preheat oven to 350°F.
**2.** In a large skillet, heat the butter or margarine and the oil, add the chicken, and brown the pieces on all sides. Season the chicken with salt and pepper and transfer it to a large casserole.
**3.** Add the onions and garlic to the skillet and cook, stirring, until the onions are translucent.
**4.** Add the bulgur to the skillet, stirring to coat it and brown it lightly.
**5.** Add the cardamom, coriander, cumin, lemon zest, and lemon juice to the bulgur mixture, mixing the ingredients well. Spoon the bulgur on top of the chicken.
**6.** Pour the boiling broth over the chicken and bulgur. Cover the casserole and bake for 1 hour or until the chicken is tender.

*Yield: 6 servings*

| Nutritive values per serving (3 ounces chicken and ½ cup bulgur): | CAL | CHO (gm) | PRO (gm) | FAT (gm) |
|---|---|---|---|---|
| | 341 | 44 | 21 | 9 |

| Food exchanges per serving (3 ounces chicken and ½ cup bulgur): | 3 BREAD, 3 medium-fat MEAT |
|---|---|

# Foiled Chicken

*Multiply this recipe by as many servings as you need for your family. No pans to clean!*

    1  tablespoon chopped fresh dill, parsley, or
       basil *or* 1 teaspoon dried
    1  clove garlic, minced
    1  boneless chicken breast half, skinned and
       cut into 4 pieces
       Freshly ground black pepper
    ½  cup broccoli flowerets, sliced carrots, or
       cauliflower flowerets
    ½  lemon

**1.** Preheat oven to 350°F.
**2.** Cut a piece of foil (about 12 inches) into large heart shape.
**3.** Mix herbs and garlic together.
**4.** Arrange chicken pieces on foil. Do not overlap pieces.
**5.** Sprinkle herb mixture and black pepper to taste over chicken.
**6.** Arrange broccoli on top of chicken.
**7.** Slice lemon and arrange on top of broccoli.
**8.** Seal package by crimping edges.
**9.** Place on baking sheet and bake for 30 minutes.
**10.** Transfer to dinner plate. Sit down, break into packet, and inhale.

*Yield: 1 serving*

| Nutritive values per serving: | CAL | CHO (gm) | PRO (gm) | FAT (gm) |
|---|---|---|---|---|
| | 190 | 5 | 23 | 9 |
| Food exchanges per serving: | 3 lean MEAT, 1 VEGETABLE | | | |

# Orange Chicken

*This is delicious and elegant enough for company.*

1 cup unsweetened orange juice
2 tablespoons peeled and minced fresh gingerroot
2 teaspoons sesame oil
2 tablespoons Dijon mustard
1 tablespoon grated orange zest
1 tablespoon grated lemon zest
4 whole cloves garlic
6 boneless chicken breast halves, skinned and boned
½ cup chicken broth (preferably homemade)
Freshly ground pepper (optional)

1. Combine first 7 ingredients in blender or food processor and whirl for 15 seconds. Pour over chicken in a shallow baking pan. Cover with plastic wrap and refrigerate overnight.
2. Preheat oven to 325°F. Remove chicken breasts from marinade, reserving marinade. Sauté breasts in chicken broth 3–4 minutes per side, over medium heat in a large skillet.
3. Transfer breasts to baking pan. Cover with a piece of parchment or wax paper cut to fit the pan. Bake for 25 minutes.
4. Meanwhile, add marinade to juices in skillet and simmer over low heat until reduced and thickened, about 15 minutes. Add a little freshly ground pepper, if you like. Pass the sauce separately.

*Yield: 6 servings*

| Nutritive values per 1-breast serving: | CAL | CHO (gm) | PRO (gm) | FAT (gm) |
|---|---|---|---|---|
| | 195 | 3 | 21 | 11 |

| Food exchanges per 1-breast serving: | 3 lean MEAT |
|---|---|

# BBQ Chicken

*This flexible recipe gives you a barbecue flavor whether you use your outdoor grill, your broiler, or your range.*

1 medium onion, chopped
1 tablespoon olive or peanut oil
1¼ cups tomato sauce
1 tablespoon Worcestershire sauce
1 tablespoon cider vinegar
1 small bay leaf
¼ teaspoon dry mustard
¼ teaspoon ground cumin
¼ teaspoon hot pepper sauce
⅛ teaspoon freshly ground pepper
1 3-pound broiler-fryer, cut into serving-size pieces and skinned

1. Sauté onion in oil in medium saucepan until tender. Stir in remaining ingredients except chicken and simmer 15 minutes. Remove bay leaf and discard.
2. Pour sauce over chicken in shallow baking dish. Cover and refrigerate for at least 4 hours, turning occasionally.
3. Grill chicken on barbecue or broil on foil-lined broiler pan 7 inches from heat. Cook 7–8 minutes on first side and 5 minutes after turning, until done. Baste often with marinade. A third cooking method: put chicken in large skillet, cover, and cook over low heat for 30 minutes. Uncover, turn chicken, and cook for another 15 minutes, until tender.

*Yield: 6 servings*

| Nutritive values per serving: | | CHO (gm) | PRO (gm) | FAT (gm) |
|---|---|---|---|---|
| | CAL | | | |
| | 152 | 4 | 16 | 8 |

Food exchanges per serving: 2 lean MEAT, 1 VEGETABLE, ½ FAT

# Oven-Fried Chicken

*The best fried chicken I ever tasted was in Texas. It was so tender and tasty that I went to the kitchen and asked the cook for her secret. She told me she marinated the chicken overnight in vinegar. Here's a low-fat version of that tasty recipe.*

    1   cup white or cider vinegar
        Skinned chicken pieces: 2 whole breasts
        (split), 2 legs and thighs
    2   eggs
    1   cup chicken broth
    1½  cups fresh whole grain bread crumbs
        (made in blender)
    ½   cup grated Parmesan cheese
    2   tablespoons paprika

**1.** The night before serving, pour vinegar over chicken. Turn to coat and cover. Refrigerate.

**2.** One hour before dinner, preheat oven to 325°F. Combine eggs and chicken broth in one shallow dish. Combine bread crumbs, cheese, and paprika in another. Dip each piece of chicken in egg, then crumbs. Bake in shallow baking dish for approximately 45 minutes.

**Variation**

Substitute 3 tablespoons sesame seeds for cheese. (The cheese and sesame seeds are approximately the same in calories and nutritional breakdown, so there is no real difference in exchanges in this variation.)

*Yield: 6 servings (1 breast or 1 leg and thigh per serving)*

| Nutritive values per serving: | CAL | CHO (gm) | PRO (gm) | FAT (gm) |
|---|---|---|---|---|
| | 347 | 30 | 29 | 12 |

Food exchanges per serving:       2 BREAD, 3½ lean MEAT, trace FAT

# Peanut Butter Chicken

*Serve with noodles or brown rice, steamed vegetables, and fresh pineapple or a lemon dessert like Lemon Snow (see index for recipe) to balance the peanut butter flavor.*

3  cloves garlic, minced
1  medium onion, sliced
1  28-ounce can tomatoes, whirled in blender
¾  cup white wine
3  pounds chicken pieces, skinned
¼  cup natural peanut butter

1. Combine all ingredients except peanut butter in large skillet and simmer, covered, 45 minutes.
2. Remove chicken. Add peanut butter. Stir and heat. Pour sauce over chicken and serve.

*Yield: 6 servings*

| Nutritive values per serving: | CAL | CHO (gm) | PRO (gm) | FAT (gm) |
|---|---|---|---|---|
| | 203 | 8 | 18 | 11 |

Food exchanges per serving:  2 lean MEAT, 1½ VEGETABLE, 1 FAT

# Chicken Pizzaiola

*I had this in the home of Cynthia Wadnola, a JDF volunteer, and it was terrific. I've reduced the fat used, but the recipe is just as good. More veggies!*

½ cup each chopped: sweet red peppers, celery, carrots, green peppers, zucchini, and yellow squash

2 cloves garlic, minced

1 medium onion, sliced

½ cup sliced fresh mushrooms

½ cup sliced pitted black olives

½ cup white wine

4 cups tomato sauce

½ teaspoon basil leaves

½ teaspoon oregano leaves

¼ cup minced fresh parsley

6 chicken breast halves, skinned and boned

2 eggs, beaten

1 cup whole grain bread crumbs (made in blender)

1 tablespoon olive oil

8 ounces part-skim mozzarella cheese, sliced in 6 even slices

1. Simmer, covered, all vegetables, olives, wine, tomato sauce, and seasonings for 1 hour.
2. Flatten breasts with a mallet. Dip in egg and then bread crumbs. Sauté in olive oil until golden on both sides. Transfer to baking dish. Preheat oven to 325°F.
3. Spoon sauce over chicken. Cover and bake for 15 minutes.
4. Uncover and place 1 slice of cheese on each breast. Spoon some sauce over the cheese and place under broiler for a few minutes, until cheese melts.

*Yield: 6 servings*

Nutritive values per serving:

| | CAL | CHO (gm) | PRO (gm) | FAT (gm) |
|---|---|---|---|---|
| | 510 | 37 | 41 | 21 |

Food exchanges per serving: 1½ BREAD, 4½ lean MEAT, 3 VEGETABLE, 1½ FAT

# Chicken Cordon Bleu

*Serve lemon wedges to squeeze over this dish.*

- 8 chicken breast halves, skinned and boned
- 8 teaspoons chopped fresh parsley
- 4 ounces part-skim mozzarella cheese, cut into 8 thin slices
- 4 ounces boiled ham, cut into 4 thin slices and halved
- 1 tablespoon diet mayonnaise
- 1 tablespoon warm water
- ¼ cup whole grain bread crumbs (made in blender)

**1.** Preheat oven to 325°F.
**2.** Pound breasts until they are thin. Sprinkle with parsley. Top each with a slice of cheese, then a half-slice of ham. Roll up tightly.
**3.** Stir together mayonnaise and water in shallow dish. Roll each chicken fillet in the mayonnaise mixture, then in the bread crumbs. Arrange the chicken rolls, seam side down, in a single layer on a nonstick or foil-lined baking sheet. Bake 20–25 minutes or until browned, cooked through, and cheese is melted.

*Yield: 8 servings*

Nutritive values per serving:

| | CAL | CHO (gm) | PRO (gm) | FAT (gm) |
|---|---|---|---|---|
| | 258 | 4 | 29 | 14 |

Food exchanges per serving: ⅓ BREAD, 4 lean MEAT, ½ FAT

# Brunswick Stew

*This is a one-pot meal that makes for easy clean-up. Lima beans are a traditional ingredient, but peas are a good substitute for the kid who says, "Limas? Ugh!" If you don't have homemade stock handy, use the low-sodium canned.*

1 roasting chicken (about 4–5 pounds), cut into serving pieces and skinned
2 cups water
4 cups homemade chicken stock
2 cups chopped celery
2 medium onions, chopped
1 cup chopped green pepper
1 clove garlic, minced
¼ cup chopped fresh parsley
1 teaspoon dried thyme
3 tablespoons Worcestershire sauce
1 teaspoon hot pepper sauce
1 28-ounce can crushed tomatoes *or* 4 large tomatoes, peeled and chopped
½ teaspoon freshly ground pepper
1 16-ounce bag frozen corn
1 10-ounce package frozen lima beans *or* peas

**1.** In Dutch oven, combine chicken, water, stock, celery, onions, green pepper, garlic, parsley, thyme, Worcestershire sauce, hot pepper sauce, tomatoes, and pepper. Bring to a boil. Reduce heat, cover, and simmer 1 hour.
**2.** Remove chicken and cool. Remove meat from bones and return to Dutch oven; discard bones. Add corn and lima beans or peas. Simmer 30 minutes.

*Yield: 8 approximately 2-cup servings*

| Nutritive values per approximate 2-cup serving: | CAL | CHO (gm) | PRO (gm) | FAT (gm) |
|---|---|---|---|---|
| | 258 | 30 | 21 | 6 |

Food exchanges per approximate
2-cup serving:     2 BREAD, 2½ lean MEAT

## TURKEY

# Turkey Loaf

*Try this instead of meat loaf.*

> 2  pounds ground turkey
> 1  cup shredded carrots
> ½  cup quick (not instant) oats
> ½  cup chopped celery
> ¼  cup chopped onion
> ¼  cup minced fresh parsley
> 1  egg
> ¼  cup water
> ½  teaspoon each: sage, thyme, marjoram, and
>    oregano leaves
> 1  teaspoon Worcestershire sauce
> ½  teaspoon freshly ground pepper
> ¼  cup catsup
> ¾  teaspoon dry mustard

**1.** Preheat oven to 350°F.
**2.** In a medium bowl, combine turkey, carrots, oats, celery, onion, parsley, egg, water, herbs, Worcestershire sauce, and pepper. Press into a 9- by 5-inch loaf pan.
**3.** In a small bowl, combine catsup and mustard. Spoon over meat loaf. Bake 45 minutes. Cut into 8 equal slices.

### *Yield: 8 servings*

| Nutritive values per serving: | CAL | CHO (gm) | PRO (gm) | FAT (gm) |
|---|---|---|---|---|
| | 200 | 8 | 24 | 8 |

Food exchanges per serving:        3 lean MEAT, 1½ VEGETABLE

# Roast Stuffed Turkey

*Roast turkey is a low-fat protein source that's easy to prepare, and I roast a whole turkey about once a month. I use the leftovers for sandwiches, soup, and Turkey Chili (see index for recipe). Also, be sure to save the turkey carcass for stock. Cover it with water and simmer for several hours. Add a few chopped carrots, celery stalks, an onion or two, and ½ lemon, sliced. Strain. Refrigerate until fat solidifies, then remove fat and use stock for soup or other recipes. Use it in any recipe that calls for chicken broth. My favorite stuffing recipe follows this one. Concerning the cooking time, it's usually recommended that you cook a stuffed turkey 15–20 minutes per pound. I have found that cooking the turkey completely covered, as I describe here, cuts the cooking time for a 12-pound turkey by 45 minutes to 1 hour. I've recommended 3–3½ hours, but it may be done before 3 hours. Start checking the thermometer after 2½ hours.*

    1  12-pound turkey, fresh or defrosted
       Freshly ground black pepper to taste
   12  cups Stuffing for Turkey (recipe follows)
    1  cup white wine
       Paprika

**1.** Preheat oven to 325°F.
**2.** Wash the bird and dry it with paper towels. Sprinkle the cavity with pepper.
**3.** Spoon in the stuffing (do not pack tightly), leaving a little space at the end for expansion. If the neck skin is available, stuff that, too. Sew up the open ends (try dental floss instead of thread) or close with skewers and cord. (That's the traditional way to do it. I don't, and I've never had stuffing fall out of a turkey.)
**4.** Place the turkey breast side up on a rack in a roasting pan big enough to hold it without squeezing it. Pour wine over, sprinkle with paprika, and cover with foil or

pan cover if it fits. Roast the bird for approximately 3–
3½ hours (or until a thermometer inserted in the bird's
thigh registers 180–185°F), removing the cover and
basting the turkey with the pan juices several times
during the last 30–60 minutes. For an unstuffed turkey, reduce the roasting time by about 30 minutes.

**5.** To serve, transfer the stuffing to a separate bowl before
carving the turkey. Serve the turkey without the skin.
Turkey skin is much less fatty than chicken but still
would add 90 calories and 2 FAT exchanges per ounce.

*Yield: 12 servings*

| Nutritive values per 5-ounce serving: | CAL | CHO (gm) | PRO (gm) | FAT (gm) |
|---|---|---|---|---|
| | 275 | 0 | 35 | 15 |

Food exchanges per 5-ounce
serving:                          5 lean MEAT

# Stuffing for Turkey

*I make the cornbread fresh or use half of a recipe that's left over from breakfast. If you're not that ambitious, use the whole wheat bread. Lots of fiber and sneaky vegetables in this one!*

> 1 recipe Gloria's Cornbread (see index for recipe) *or* 1 1-pound loaf whole wheat bread *or* ½ recipe Gloria's Cornbread and ½ loaf whole wheat bread
> ¼ cup minced fresh parsley
> 2 medium apples, cored, unpeeled, and chopped
> 2 medium onions, chopped
> 3 stalks celery, diced
> 3 medium carrots, grated
> ¼ head green cabbage, chopped
> 1 cup chicken broth
> 1 teaspoon basil leaves
> 2 teaspoons sage leaves
> Freshly ground pepper

1. Crumble the bread or cornbread by hand or cut it into cubes.
2. Sauté the apple and the vegetables with chicken broth for 10 minutes over medium heat.
3. Combine all ingredients in a large bowl. (You'll probably have more stuffing than the turkey can hold. Put it into a 1-quart casserole, sprinkle with ¼ cup skim milk, cover, and bake at 325°F for 40–45 minutes.)

*Yield: 12 servings*

| Nutritive values with Whole Wheat Bread, per serving: | CAL | CHO (gm) | PRO (gm) | FAT (gm) |
|---|---|---|---|---|
| | 116 | 25 | 4 | 0 |

Food exchanges with Whole Wheat
Bread, per serving:          1⅔ BREAD

| Nutritive values with ½ bread and ½ cornbread, per serving: | CAL | CHO (gm) | PRO (gm) | FAT (gm) |
|---|---|---|---|---|
| | 141 | 27 | 5 | 1 |

Food exchanges with ½ bread and ½ cornbread, per serving:          2 BREAD, trace FAT

| Nutritive values with cornbread, per serving: | CAL | CHO (gm) | PRO (gm) | FAT (gm) |
|---|---|---|---|---|
| | 167 | 29 | 6 | 3 |

Food exchanges with cornbread, per serving:          2 BREAD, ½ FAT

# Turkey Burgers

*Try these as a low-fat alternative to hamburgers.*

    1  pound ground turkey
    ½  cup whole grain bread crumbs (made in
       blender from 2 slices bread)
    2  tablespoons finely chopped onion
    2  tablespoons fresh lemon juice
    1  teaspoon Worcestershire sauce
    ½  teaspoon paprika
       Freshly ground black pepper to taste

**1.** Combine all ingredients and shape the mixture into 6 patties.
**2.** Fry, broil, or grill the burgers until they are done, about 5 minutes a side.

*Yield: 6 servings*

| Nutritive values per serving: | CAL | CHO (gm) | PRO (gm) | FAT (gm) |
|---|---|---|---|---|
| | 138 | 6 | 15 | 6 |

Food exchanges per serving:          ⅓ BREAD, 2 lean MEAT

# Turkey Tetrazzini

*Here's one good way to use leftover turkey.*

¼ pound mushrooms, sliced
1 tablespoon diet margarine
2 tablespoons unbleached white flour
½ teaspoon salt
½ teaspoon freshly ground pepper
⅛ teaspoon cayenne pepper
2 cups skim milk
1 teaspoon Worcestershire sauce
½ cup shredded Swiss or Gruyère cheese
⅓ cup sliced green onions
2 cups cooked turkey or chicken (about
   ½ pound), cut into small cubes
½ pound spaghetti, cooked al dente and
   drained
¼ cup grated Parmesan cheese

1. Preheat oven to 350°F.
2. In a large saucepan over medium heat, sauté the mushrooms in the margarine, stirring them often, until they are just tender.
3. Stir in the flour, salt, pepper, and cayenne. Gradually add the milk, stirring constantly. Add the Worcestershire sauce and simmer the sauce, stirring, until it has thickened.
4. Add the cheese and green onions to the sauce and mix well. Add half the sauce to the turkey and half to the spaghetti.
5. Place the spaghetti in the bottom of a greased 2-quart baking dish. Make a well in the center and pour in the turkey. Sprinkle with Parmesan cheese.
6. Bake for 20 minutes, until heated through.

*Yield: 6 1-cup servings*

| Nutritive values per 1-cup serving: | CAL | CHO (gm) | PRO (gm) | FAT (gm) |
|---|---|---|---|---|
| | 287 | 35 | 21 | 7 |

Food exchanges per 1-cup serving:    2½ BREAD, 2 lean MEAT, trace FAT

# FISH

The secret to properly cooked fish is timing. Overcooking toughens and dries it. The rule the professionals use is called the "10-minute rule": cook 10 minutes per inch of thickness. As fish cooks, it turns from translucent to opaque, like egg whites. To test if it's done, insert a fork at its thickest point, and if the fish looks opaque, it's ready. If it flakes easily, you've probably overcooked it. Fish that is baked, simmered, or enclosed in foil takes longer than fish that's broiled, fried, or poached. Use a 15-minute rule in that case.

# Seafood Stew

*This is actually a very easy bouillabaisse.*

1 cup chopped onion
1 clove garlic, minced
2 cups chopped fresh tomatoes
2 10½-ounce cans condensed beef broth (preferably low-sodium)
½ cup cream sherry
4 lemon slices
3 whole allspice
1 bay leaf
1 pound skinned fish fillets
1 pound shrimp, deveined
1 dozen clams *or* 1 10-ounce can chopped clams, undrained
¼ cup grated Parmesan cheese

**1.** Simmer onion, garlic, tomatoes, beef broth, sherry, lemon slices, and seasonings, uncovered, for 30 minutes.
**2.** Cut fish fillets into large chunks. Add fish, shrimp, and clams to pot. Simmer 15–20 minutes or until clams open. Top with grated Parmesan cheese. Serve with salad and garlic bread.

*Yield: 6 1½-cup servings*

| Nutritive values per 1½-cup serving: | CAL | CHO (gm) | PRO (gm) | FAT (gm) |
|---|---|---|---|---|
| | 199 | 5 | 38 | 3 |

| Food exchanges per 1½-cup serving: | 5½ lean MEAT, 1 VEGETABLE |
|---|---|

# Oven "French-Fried" Scallops

*Many kids, including my own, love these easy and tasty scallops.*

> 1 pound fresh or frozen and defrosted scallops
> ½ cup low-calorie Italian dressing
> ½ cup fresh whole grain bread crumbs (make in blender or food processor from 2 slices bread)
> Paprika
> Lemon slices

**1.** Preheat oven to 450°F.
**2.** Drain scallops and pat dry with a paper towel. Dip in dressing, then roll in bread crumbs. Sprinkle with paprika. For best results, refrigerate and allow to dry before baking.
**3.** Spread scallops in single layer in nonstick baking pan or cookie sheet. Bake 10 minutes per inch of thickness. Serve with lemon wedges.

*Yield: 4 3-ounce servings*

| Nutritive values per 3-ounce serving: | CAL | CHO (gm) | PRO (gm) | FAT (gm) |
|---|---|---|---|---|
| | 155 | 10 | 22 | 3 |

| Food exchanges per 3-ounce serving: | ⅔ BREAD, 3 lean MEAT |
|---|---|

# Saucy Scallops

1½ cups water
1 cup dry white wine
¼ teaspoon salt
2 tablespoons minced onion
Dash freshly ground pepper
1 pound fresh bay or sea scallops
1 cup sliced fresh mushrooms
2 tablespoons diet margarine
2 tablespoons all-purpose flour
1 cup skim milk
¼ teaspoon freshly ground white pepper
½ cup shredded Swiss cheese
1 teaspoon Dijon mustard
2 tablespoons chopped fresh parsley
2 tablespoons minced fresh dill *or* 2
teaspoons dried dillweed

1. Preheat oven to 375°F.
2. Combine first 5 ingredients in a medium saucepan; cover and simmer 5 minutes. Stir scallops and mushrooms into liquid mixture; cover and simmer 5 minutes.
3. Remove scallops and mushrooms from saucepan with a slotted spoon, reserving liquid in pan; set scallops and mushrooms aside. Bring liquid to a boil and cook, uncovered, 10 minutes or until liquid is reduced to about 1 cup.
4. Melt margarine in a heavy saucepan over low heat; add flour and cook 1 minute, stirring constantly (mixture will be dry). Gradually add 1 cup reduced liquid and milk to flour mixture; cook over medium heat, stirring constantly with a wire whisk, until thickened and bubbly. Add white pepper, cheese, mustard, parsley, and dill, stirring until cheese is melted.
5. Spoon scallops, mushrooms, and sauce into 1-quart casserole and brown under broiler for 3–4 minutes or until sauce turns golden brown and begins to bubble.

*Yield: 4 1-cup servings*

| Nutritive values per 1-cup serving: | CAL | CHO (gm) | PRO (gm) | FAT (gm) |
|---|---|---|---|---|
| | 228 | 9 | 30 | 8 |

Food exchanges per 1-cup serving:          ½ BREAD, 4 lean MEAT

# Foiled Fish Fillets

*Here's an easy recipe for fish from Lanna Saunders, a wonderful actress and a very good cook.*

1⅓  pounds red snapper fillets
4  small pieces peeled fresh gingerroot
4  teaspoons soy sauce
4  shallots, minced, or green onions, chopped

**1.** Preheat oven to 400°F.
**2.** Cut or divide fish into 4 equal portions. Place each on a square of heavy-duty aluminum foil. Top each with a slice of ginger, 1 teaspoon soy sauce, and 1 shallot or green onion.
**3.** Seal foil like an envelope. Bake for 10–12 minutes.

**Variations**
**1.** Use sole or other firm white fish and to each portion add 1 tablespoon fresh lemon juice and 1 tablespoon minced fresh parsley with green onion; omit ginger and soy sauce.
**2.** Use salmon fillets with 2 tablespoons vermouth; ¼ teaspoon dill; ½ clove garlic, minced; 1 green onion; and 1 new potato, cut into small pieces, on each. (For this variation, add 1 BREAD and 70 calories.)

*Yield: 4 servings*

| Nutritive values per serving: | CAL | CHO (gm) | PRO (gm) | FAT (gm) |
|---|---|---|---|---|
| | 185 | 2 | 33 | 5 |

Food exchanges per serving:          4½ lean MEAT

# Oven Fish Fillets

1 8-ounce carton nonfat yogurt
¼ cup grated Parmesan cheese
2 tablespoons minced fresh parsley
½ onion, minced
3 tablespoons fresh lemon juice
1 clove garlic, minced
1 pound flounder or other fish fillets

1. Preheat oven to 375°F.
2. Combine first 6 ingredients in blender or food processor. Whirl just until smooth. Place fish in baking dish; spread sauce evenly over fillets.
3. Bake for 12–15 minutes. Fish should separate easily when a fork is inserted in the middle.

*Yield: 4 3-ounce servings*

| Nutritive values per 3-ounce serving: | CAL | CHO (gm) | PRO (gm) | FAT (gm) |
|---|---|---|---|---|
| | 152 | 4 | 25 | 4 |

Food exchanges per 3-ounce
serving:                          ⅓ MILK, 3 lean MEAT

# Salmon Croquettes

*A lady named Mercedes Cornell who worked for me used to make these, and the boys loved them and still do.*

1 7¾-ounce can salmon, drained and flaked
¼ cup bread crumbs (made in blender or food processor from 1 slice whole grain bread)
2 eggs, slightly beaten
2 tablespoons fresh lemon juice
¼ teaspoon freshly ground pepper
1 teaspoon dried dillweed *or* 1 tablespoon minced fresh dill
  Olive oil
½ cup finely chopped celery
⅓ cup finely chopped green onions
  Mustard Sauce (recipe follows)

1. Combine first 6 ingredients; set aside.
2. Coat a large nonstick skillet with 1 teaspoon olive oil; place over medium heat until hot. Add celery and green onions; sauté until tender. Add to salmon mixture; mix well.
3. Coat skillet again with $\frac{1}{2}$ teaspoon olive oil; place over medium-high heat until hot. For each salmon cake, spoon about $\frac{1}{4}$ cup mixture onto skillet; shape into patty with a spatula. Cook about 2 minutes or until browned on each side. Serve immediately with Mustard Sauce (recipe follows).

*Yield: 4 servings (2 croquettes each)*

| Nutritive values per 2-croquette serving: | CAL | CHO (gm) | PRO (gm) | FAT (gm) |
|---|---|---|---|---|
| | 208 | 12 | 22 | 8 |

Food exchanges per 2-croquette serving: 1 BREAD, 3 lean MEAT

# Mustard Sauce

2 tablespoons diet margarine
$1\frac{1}{2}$ tablespoons unbleached white flour
1 cup skim milk
1 teaspoon Dijon mustard
1 tablespoon fresh lemon juice
$\frac{1}{4}$ teaspoon salt

1. Melt margarine over low heat; add flour, stirring until smooth. Cook 1 minute, stirring constantly.
2. Gradually add milk; cook over medium heat, stirring constantly, until thickened and bubbly. Remove from heat; stir in mustard, lemon juice, and salt.

*Yield: 1 cup*

| Nutritive values per 2-tablespoon serving: | CAL | CHO (gm) | PRO (gm) | FAT (gm) |
|---|---|---|---|---|
| | 30 | 2 | 11 | 2 |

Food exchanges per 2-tablespoon serving: $\frac{1}{2}$ FAT

# MEAT DISHES

Meat is an excellent source of protein and the B vitamins as well as iron. Use lean choices with all visible fat trimmed. Serve meat with lots of side dishes so that the meat doesn't become the focal point of the meal.

## BEEF

# Lean Pastichio

*This is a Greek dish of beef and pasta with a low-fat cheese sauce. Feta cheese is very strong and interesting in flavor, but some children may find it too strong. It can also be very salty. Try soaking it in cold water for 20 minutes, then draining, to rid it of some salt.*

    ¾  pound lean ground round
    ½  cup chopped onion
    1  cup uncooked elbow macaroni (whole
       wheat, if possible)
    1  8-ounce can low-sodium tomato sauce
    2  tablespoons grated Parmesan cheese
    1  medium zucchini, diced
    ½  teaspoon thyme leaves
    ¼  teaspoon ground cinnamon
    ½  cup skim milk
    3  tablespoons unbleached white flour
    ¼  teaspoon white pepper
    1  cup skim milk
    ¼  cup plus 2 tablespoons grated Parmesan
       cheese
    ½  cup crumbled feta cheese (optional)
    2  eggs, beaten
       Ground cinnamon

**1.** Preheat oven to 375°F.
**2.** Cook meat and onion in a large nonstick skillet over

medium-high heat until meat is browned; drain meat in a colander and pat dry with paper towels.

3. Cook macaroni according to package directions, omitting salt. Combine meat mixture, macaroni, and next 5 ingredients; spread in bottom of a 10- by 6- by 2-inch baking dish.

4. Combine ½ cup milk, flour, and pepper in a jar; cover tightly and shake vigorously to blend. Pour into a small saucepan and stir in 1 cup milk. Cook over medium heat, stirring constantly, until mixture is thickened and bubbly. Remove from heat and stir in ¼ cup plus 2 tablespoons Parmesan cheese and feta cheese. Let cool to room temperature.

5. Stir eggs into thickened milk mixture; pour evenly over meat mixture. Sprinkle lightly with cinnamon. Bake for 30–35 minutes or until knife inserted near center comes out clean. Let stand 10 minutes before serving. Divide into 6 equal portions.

*Yield: 6 approximately 1-cup servings*

| Nutritive values without feta, per approximately 1-cup serving: | CAL | CHO (gm) | PRO (gm) | FAT (gm) |
|---|---|---|---|---|
| | 263 | 21 | 20 | 11 |

| Food exchanges without feta, per approximately 1-cup serving: | 1 BREAD, 2 medium-fat MEAT 1 VEGETABLE | | | |
|---|---|---|---|---|

| Nutritive values with feta, per approximately 1-cup serving: | CAL | CHO (gm) | PRO (gm) | FAT (gm) |
|---|---|---|---|---|
| | 289 | 21 | 22 | 13 |

| Food exchanges with feta, per approximately 1-cup serving: | 1 BREAD, 2½ medium-fat MEAT, 1 VEGETABLE | | | |
|---|---|---|---|---|

# Beef and Tomato Stir-Fry

*My boys first had this at their grandma's and cleaned their plates.*

1  pound lean top round steak, sliced thin across the grain
1  tablespoon cornstarch
2  tablespoons soy sauce (preferably reduced-sodium)
1  tablespoon peeled and minced fresh gingerroot
1  clove garlic, minced
1  teaspoon dark sesame oil
2  green onions, sliced thin
1  medium red pepper, cut into 1-inch chunks
1  medium green pepper, cut into 1-inch chunks
1  tablespoon water
1  medium zucchini, cut into ¼-inch slices
3  large tomatoes, seeded and cut into wedges
1  cup tomato juice
2  teaspoons Worcestershire sauce
3  cups hot, cooked rice

1. Place beef in a large, shallow glass baking dish. In small bowl, combine cornstarch, soy sauce, ginger, and garlic. Pour over beef; cover and marinate several hours or overnight.
2. In large skillet, heat oil. Stir-fry meat in batches until browned. Remove meat and reserve. Add green onion, red and green pepper, and 1 tablespoon water to skillet; cover and cook 1 minute. Add zucchini; cover and cook 1 minute.
3. Add tomatoes and meat to skillet.
4. Add tomato juice and Worcestershire sauce to skillet; stir to combine well. Cook until thickened. Serve over rice.

*Yield: 4 servings (1¼ cups plus ¾ cup rice each)*

| Nutritive values per serving (1¼ cups plus ¾ cup rice): | CAL | CHO (gm) | PRO (gm) | FAT (gm) |
|---|---|---|---|---|
| | 350 | 36 | 29 | 10 |

Food exchanges per serving
(1¼ cups plus ¾ cup rice): ½ BREAD, 3 lean MEAT, 3 VEGETABLE

# Oriental Flank Steak

*I serve this with Chinese Vegetables (see index for recipe) and Korean rice, and it's one of our favorite meals.*

2 tablespoons dark sesame oil
3 cloves garlic, minced
¾ teaspoon ground ginger *or* 2 slices peeled fresh gingerroot, minced
½ cup low-sodium soy sauce *or* ¼ cup regular soy sauce and ¼ cup water
½ cup cream sherry
4 green onions, chopped
2 flank steaks (approximately 1¼ pounds each)

The night before serving, combine first 6 ingredients and pour over steaks in a shallow pan. Turn once or twice. The next day, broil steaks 6–7 minutes per side. (I use an indoor BBQ-type broiler.) Meanwhile, heat the marinade for 10–15 minutes. Slice the steaks thin across the grain, diagonally (à la London Broil) and pour marinade over to serve.

*Yield: 8 4-ounce servings*

| Nutritive values per 4-ounce serving: | CAL | CHO (gm) | PRO (gm) | FAT (gm) |
|---|---|---|---|---|
| | 250 | 0 | 28 | 15 |

Food exchanges per 4-ounce serving: 4 lean MEAT, ½ FAT

# Beef and Snow Peas

*Chinese stir-fry dishes are great because they are made in one pan, have lots of vegetables, are low-fat, and cook quickly. See if you can get Korean rice. It has a round kernel and is slightly transparent. It's sometimes available in large supermarkets. Oyster sauce is available in Oriental markets and some supermarkets.*

1 pound flank steak, semifrozen, cut into thin slices across grain
2 tablespoons cream sherry
2 tablespoons rice vinegar
2 tablespoons soy sauce (preferably reduced-sodium)
2 tablespoons cornstarch
2 teaspoons dark sesame oil
1 pound Chinese pea pods, stem ends cut off
¼ head green cabbage, chopped
¼ pound mushrooms, cleaned and sliced
1 teaspoon dark sesame oil
2 slices peeled fresh gingerroot, minced
1 clove garlic, minced
2 tablespoons broth or water
1 tablespoon oyster sauce

1. Marinate steak in sherry, vinegar, soy sauce, and cornstarch overnight in refrigerator.
2. Heat 2 teaspoons sesame oil in wok or large skillet until hot. Add pea pods, cabbage, and mushrooms. Stir-fry a few minutes. Remove vegetables and reserve.
3. Add 1 teaspoon sesame oil to wok and stir-fry ginger and garlic for 1 minute. Add steak to wok and stir-fry until the steak loses its pinkness. Add vegetables, broth, and oyster sauce. Cover and steam for 1 minute.

*Yield: 6 1-cup servings*

| Nutritive values per 1-cup serving: | CAL | CHO (gm) | PRO (gm) | FAT (gm) |
|---|---|---|---|---|
| | 164 | 7 | 16 | 8 |

Food exchanges per 1-cup serving: 2 lean MEAT, 1½ VEGETABLE, ½ FAT

# Pot Roast

*I use a seven-bone, round-bone, or top round roast.*

- 1 3-pound beef pot roast, trimmed of visible fat
- 1 lemon
- 2 medium onions, sliced thin
- 6 small carrots
- 1 clove garlic, minced
- 2 medium unpeeled potatoes, quartered
- 1 teaspoon dry mustard
- 1 teaspoon ground ginger
- 1 teaspoon thyme leaves
- 4 stalks celery, with leaves, chopped
- 1 small green pepper, cut up
- 2 cups tomato *or* vegetable juice

1. The night before serving, put roast in a glass casserole and squeeze lemon over it. Pierce with a fork, cover tightly, and refrigerate.
2. Preheat oven to 325°F about 3 hours before dinner.
3. Put roast in large casserole with a cover. Put onions, carrots, garlic, and potatoes around meat. Sprinkle mustard, ginger, and thyme over meat. Place celery and green pepper on top of meat.
4. Pour tomato or vegetable juice around meat. Cover and bake until fork-tender, about 3 hours.

*Yield: 6 4½-ounce servings*

| Nutritive values per 4½-ounce serving: | CAL | CHO (gm) | PRO (gm) | FAT (gm) |
|---|---|---|---|---|
| | 378 | 11 | 34 | 22 |

Food exchanges per 4½-ounce serving: 1 BREAD, 4½ medium-fat MEAT

# Vegetable and Meat Loaf

*Using lean ground round instead of ground beef decreases the amount of fat and calories, especially when cooked in the manner described below. Use a baster to siphon off the liquefied fats and juices that collect in the pan during cooking. More fiber, less meat!*

1½ pounds lean ground round
½ cup soft whole wheat bread crumbs (made in blender)
½ cup shredded carrots
¼ cup thinly sliced celery
½ onion, minced
¼ cup chopped green pepper
1 egg, slightly beaten
1 small bunch fresh spinach, cleaned, stemmed, and chopped (½ pound)
2 teaspoons Worcestershire sauce
½ teaspoon dry mustard
½ teaspoon freshly ground pepper
2 tablespoons minced fresh parsley
¼ cup tomato puree
1 16-ounce can whole tomatoes
1 teaspoon basil leaves

1. Preheat oven to 350°F.
2. Combine all ingredients except tomato puree, tomatoes, and basil. Shape into a loaf. Place in shallow baking dish. Pour puree over and bake for 1 hour or until done.
3. Whirl the tomatoes briefly in a blender or food processor. There should still be some small lumps of tomato. Add the basil. Transfer to a small saucepan and simmer, uncovered, for 10–15 minutes. Serve the sauce separately.
4. Lift meat loaf out of drippings with 2 large spatulas. Cut into 6 equal portions. They will be approximately ¾ cup in volume.

*Yield: 6 servings*

| Nutritive values per serving: | | CHO | PRO | FAT |
|---|---|---|---|---|
| | CAL | (gm) | (gm) | (gm) |
| | 213 | 12 | 22 | 9 |

Food exchanges per serving:              3 lean MEAT, 1 VEGETABLE

# Swiss Steak

1  2-pound round steak
3  tablespoons unbleached white flour
$\frac{1}{2}$  teaspoon salt
$\frac{1}{2}$  teaspoon freshly ground pepper
$\frac{1}{2}$  teaspoon paprika
1  tablespoon olive oil
1  medium onion, chopped
$\frac{1}{2}$  cup each chopped carrots, celery, and green pepper
$\frac{1}{4}$  cup chopped fresh parsley
1  16-ounce can tomatoes with liquid
1  cup sliced fresh mushrooms
1  tablespoon cornstarch
$\frac{1}{4}$  cup cold water

1. Trim fat and bone from meat and cut into 6 equal portions. Mix flour, salt, pepper, and paprika and sprinkle over both sides of the meat. Pound in with a mallet or the edge of a plate. Brown meat in oil in a large skillet.
2. Add onion, carrots, celery, green pepper, parsley, and tomatoes. Cover and simmer for 2 hours. Add mushrooms for the last 10 minutes.
3. Remove meat from pan and add the cornstarch that has been stirred into the water to the skillet. Cook over medium heat, stirring, until thickened. Serve sauce over meat portions.

*Yield: 6 servings*

| Nutritive values per serving: | | CHO | PRO | FAT |
|---|---|---|---|---|
| | CAL | (gm) | (gm) | (gm) |
| | 302 | 13 | 31 | 14 |

Food exchanges per serving:              $\frac{1}{2}$ BREAD, 4 lean MEAT, 1 VEGETABLE, $\frac{1}{2}$ FAT

# Superb Oven Stew

*This is my mother's recipe, but I added the carrots, potatoes, and peas. Try serving steamed broccoli and a salad to complete the meal.*

2 pounds lean beef, cut into 1-inch cubes
½ cup unbleached white flour
2 tablespoons olive oil
2 medium onions cut into ¼-inch slices
3 cloves garlic, minced or pressed
¼ cup chopped fresh parsley
½ teaspoon thyme leaves
1½ cups beef stock (preferably low-sodium)
1 cup beer
6 carrots, cut into 1-inch chunks
3 unpeeled medium potatoes, quartered
1 cup frozen green peas
1 tablespoon wine vinegar

1. Preheat oven to 325°F.
2. Coat meat with flour and brown in oil in heavy skillet.
3. Layer meat and onions in 2-quart casserole.
4. Sauté garlic in skillet. Add parsley, thyme, and beef stock. Scrape bottom of pan to loosen meat particles. Pour over meat in casserole. Pour beer over meat.
5. Cover casserole and bake for 1½ hours. Add carrots and potatoes and bake for 45 minutes more, covered. Add peas and wine vinegar, stir in, and bake, uncovered, for 10–15 minutes.

*Yield: 6 1½-cup servings*

| Nutritive values per 1½-cup serving: | CAL | CHO (gm) | PRO (gm) | FAT (gm) |
|---|---|---|---|---|
| | 352 | 29 | 32 | 12 |

| Food exchanges per 1½-cup serving: | 2 BREAD, 4 lean MEAT |
|---|---|

## VEAL

# Veal Scaloppine

1 pound ¼-inch-thick veal cutlets
3 tablespoons unbleached white flour
½ teaspoon salt
½ teaspoon freshly ground pepper
1 tablespoon olive oil
⅔ cup Chablis or other dry white wine
2 teaspoons Dijon mustard
¼ cup fresh lemon juice
Lemon zest twists (optional)

1. Trim excess fat from veal; place veal on a sheet of wax paper. Flatten to ⅛-inch thickness, using a meat mallet or rolling pin; cut into 2-inch pieces. Combine flour, salt, and pepper; dredge veal in flour mixture.
2. Add oil to a large skillet and place over medium-high heat until hot. Add veal and cook 1 minute on each side or until lightly browned. Remove veal from skillet and set aside.
3. Pour wine, mustard, and lemon juice into skillet; bring to a boil. Return veal to skillet, turning to coat with sauce; reduce heat, and simmer 1–2 minutes or until sauce is slightly thickened and veal is thoroughly heated. Garnish with lemon twists, if desired. Divide into 4 equal portions.

*Yield: 4 servings*

| Nutritive values per serving: | CAL | CHO (gm) | PRO (gm) | FAT (gm) |
|---|---|---|---|---|
| | 220 | 6 | 22 | 12 |

Food exchanges per serving:  ⅓ BREAD, 3 lean MEAT, ½ FAT

# Osso Buco

*This classic dish is also known as Baked Marrow Bones or Braised Veal Shinbones. Serve with noodles and steamed vegetables and Carrot-Acorn Squash (see index).*

1 tablespoon extra-virgin olive oil
4 pounds veal shanks (or shinbones), cut into 2-inch chunks and trimmed of fat
2 onions, chopped
1 clove garlic, minced
2 bay leaves
1 teaspoon rosemary leaves
½ teaspoon freshly ground pepper
1 cup dry white wine vinegar
1 carrot, grated
1 celery stalk, minced
2 tablespoons red wine
1 tablespoon grated lemon zest
¼ cup chopped fresh parsley
2 cups chopped fresh tomatoes
2 tablespoons tomato paste
½ cup water or stock

1. Preheat oven to 325°F.
2. Using a Dutch oven, heat olive oil over medium-high heat and sear the cut sides of the veal shanks. Add the onions, garlic, bay leaves, rosemary, pepper, and white wine vinegar. Cover and reduce heat to low. Simmer for 5 minutes.
3. Add the carrot, celery, red wine, lemon zest, parsley, and tomatoes. Stir the tomato paste into the water or stock and add to the veal. Mix well.
4. Transfer covered Dutch oven to oven and bake for 1½–2 hours, until tender. Remove the veal and place on serving platter. Discard the bay leaves.

**5.** Over medium-high heat, cook the remaining sauce for several minutes to reduce the volume and to thicken. Pour the sauce over the shanks and serve.

*Yield: 8 1-cup servings*

| Nutritive values per 1-cup serving: | CAL | CHO (gm) | PRO (gm) | FAT (gm) |
|---|---|---|---|---|
| | 189 | 4 | 23 | 9 |

| Food exchanges per 1-cup serving: | 3 lean MEAT, 1 VEGETABLE |
|---|---|

# Veal Chops with Raspberry Vinegar

*This is a gourmet recipe that I included mainly for special occasions, because veal chops can be expensive for a family meal.*

> 4 loin veal chops ($\frac{3}{4}$–1 inch thick)
> $\frac{1}{2}$ teaspoon salt
> $\frac{1}{2}$ teaspoon freshly ground pepper
> 1 tablespoon unsalted butter
> 4 whole garlic cloves, unpeeled
> 2 bay leaves
> $\frac{1}{2}$ teaspoon thyme leaves
> 1 tablespoon raspberry vinegar
> 1 cup chicken broth
> 1 tablespoon arrowroot
> 1 tablespoon cold water

1. Sprinkle chops with salt and pepper. Heat butter in large skillet and add chops. Brown on both sides, turning once, about 5 minutes on each side. Add garlic, bay leaves, and thyme and cook 3 minutes.
2. Pour the vinegar around the chops and turn heat to high for a few seconds, turning chops to coat both sides. Turn heat down to simmer, adding $\frac{1}{2}$ cup of broth, and cook, covered tightly, for 20 minutes. Turn the chops frequently and add a little more broth when necessary, saving some for last.
3. When done, remove garlic and bay leaves and place chops on a warm platter. Mix about a teaspoon of arrowroot with 1 tablespoon cold water. Add remaining broth to the skillet and slowly add arrowroot mixture until the sauce reaches desired thickness. (Use more or less arrowroot mixture according to your taste.) Spoon sauce over chops and serve at once.

*Yield: 4 servings*

Nutritive values per serving:

| | CAL | CHO (gm) | PRO (gm) | FAT (gm) |
|---|---|---|---|---|
| | 192 | 0 | 21 | 12 |

Food exchanges per serving: 3 lean MEAT, ½ FAT

## LAMB

# Greek Lamb Chops

*Try serving this with a whole grain side dish like bulgur or kasha (buckwheat groats).*

4 ¾-inch-thick lean loin lamb chops, trimmed of fat
Juice of 1 lemon
1 tablespoon crushed dried mint leaves
⅛ teaspoon ground cinnamon
⅛ teaspoon ground nutmeg
Fresh mint sprigs (optional)

Sprinkle chops with lemon juice and seasonings; puncture repeatedly with a fork. Wrap in plastic; refrigerate several hours. Broil or grill chops, turning once, until brown and crisp outside but still pink in the middle or until done as desired. Garnish with fresh mint sprigs, if desired.

*Yield: 4 servings*

Nutritive values per serving:

| | CAL | CHO (gm) | PRO (gm) | FAT (gm) |
|---|---|---|---|---|
| | 165 | 0 | 21 | 9 |

Food exchanges per serving: 3 lean MEAT

# Lovely Lamb Stew

*This is a low-calorie main dish from the* Days of Our Lives Celebrity Cookbook, *contributed by Kaye Stevens, and published by Gloria Loring, 1981.*

1 teaspoon oil
2 pounds stewing lamb, cut into 2-inch cubes
½ cup unbleached white flour
1 teaspoon freshly ground pepper
2 cloves garlic, minced
2 teaspoons celery seeds
3 carrots, quartered
6 small white onions, halved
¼ cup minced fresh parsley
2 teaspoons Worcestershire sauce
3 cups tomato juice

Heat heavy, deep pan, greased lightly with oil. Dip lamb in flour. Brown well. Add all remaining ingredients. Cover and simmer until fork-tender, 1½–2 hours.

*Yield: 6 1¼-cup servings*

| Nutritive values per 1¼-cup serving: | CAL | CHO (gm) | PRO (gm) | FAT (gm) |
|---|---|---|---|---|
| | 293 | 14 | 30 | 13 |

Food exchanges per 1¼-cup serving:                    1 BREAD, 4 lean MEAT

# Baked Lamb Chops

4  ½-inch-thick loin lamb chops
1  tablespoon olive oil
½  cup unsweetened orange juice
2  tablespoons soy sauce (preferably low-
   sodium)
1  teaspoon ground ginger
2  cloves garlic, minced
¼  teaspoon freshly ground pepper
2  small oranges, peeled and sectioned

1. Trim excess fat from chops. Lightly brown chops in hot
   oil and drain on paper towels.
2. Place chops in a shallow baking dish. Combine orange
   juice, soy sauce, ginger, garlic, and pepper; pour marinade over chops. Cover with foil and refrigerate for 2
   hours, turning once.
3. Remove from refrigerator, but do not uncover. Bake at
   350°F for 45–55 minutes or until chops are tender.
   Place orange sections on chops, cover, and bake for 10
   minutes more. Or grill the chops, reserving the marinade. In that case, heat the marinade and pass
   separately.

*Yield: 4 servings*

| Nutritive values per serving: | CAL | CHO (gm) | PRO (gm) | FAT (gm) |
|---|---|---|---|---|
| | 224 | 8 | 21 | 11 |

Food exchanges per serving:    1 FRUIT, 3 lean MEAT, ½ FAT

## PORK
# Orange Pork Chops with Rice

*A delicious, almost one-dish meal. Serve with Broccoli Parmesan and Fruit Spiced Carrots (see index for recipes).*

 4 ¾-inch-thick pork chops
 1 teaspoon olive oil
 1 cup long-grain brown rice
 1½ cups unsweetened orange juice
 1 small onion, chopped
 ½ teaspoon ground cinnamon
 ¼ teaspoon ground nutmeg
 ½ teaspoon freshly ground pepper
 1 large baking apple, unpeeled, cored, and cut crosswise into 4 slices
   Grated zest of ½ orange
 1 orange, peeled and cut into bite-size pieces
 2 tablespoons chopped fresh parsley

1. Trim excess fat from chops. Brown in oil in large skillet. Remove chops and wipe out any fat.
2. Place next 6 ingredients in skillet and bring to boil. Reduce heat and place chops over rice. Cover and cook for 20 minutes over low heat.
3. Place an apple slice on top of each chop. Cook 15 minutes longer, until all liquid is absorbed.
4. Remove chops and apple. Stir in orange zest, orange pieces, and parsley. Arrange rice mixture and chops topped with apples on a serving dish.

*Yield: 4 servings*

| Nutritive values per serving: | CAL | CHO (gm) | PRO (gm) | FAT (gm) |
|---|---|---|---|---|
| | 360 | 32 | 31 | 12 |

Food exchanges per serving:          1½ BREAD, 1 FRUIT, 4 lean MEAT

# NOODLES, RICE, GRAINS, AND POTATOES
## Noodle Kugel

*This is another recipe from my mom that's been adjusted to be low-fat and low-sugar. My mother was born in Minnesota, of Norwegian descent, but I think she always secretly wanted to be a Jewish mother. She makes great noodle kugel and matzo ball soup! This is a good side dish for baked chicken; add a salad or steamed vegetables.*

1 8-ounce package broad egg noodles
2 whole eggs
2 egg whites
8 packets artificial sweetener (equal to ⅓ cup sugar)
1 cup nonfat yogurt
1 cup low-fat cottage cheese
¾ cup evaporated skim milk
½ cup seedless raisins *or* ¼ cup raisins and ¼ cup diced dried apricots or currants
1 teaspoon vanilla extract
½ teaspoon ground cinnamon
¼ teaspoon ground nutmeg
1 teaspoon grated orange zest

**1.** Preheat oven to 350°F.
**2.** Cook noodles according to package directions. Drain.
**3.** In a large bowl, beat eggs, egg whites, and sweetener. Blend in all remaining ingredients. Add noodles and mix thoroughly.
**4.** Pour into a 2-quart baking dish and bake 1 hour.

*Yield: 8 ¾-cup servings*

| Nutritive values per ¾-cup serving: | CAL | CHO (gm) | PRO (gm) | FAT (gm) |
|---|---|---|---|---|
| | 200 | 30 | 13 | 3 |

| Food exchanges per ¾-cup serving: | |
|---|---|
| | 2 BREAD, 1 FRUIT, 1 lean MEAT |

# Red Beans and Rice

*This dish is very good for many reasons. First of all, it's very high in fiber. Also, the combination of beans and rice makes this a complete protein. It can be served as a main dish with a salad and vegetable dish for a very nutritious meal.*

      ¾  pound ham hocks
      1  quart water
      1  pound dried red beans
      1½ cups chopped onion
      1  cup chopped fresh parsley
      1  cup chopped green pepper
      ½  cup chopped green onions
      2  cloves garlic, pressed
      1  8-ounce can tomato sauce
      1  tablespoon Worcestershire sauce
      1  teaspoon freshly ground pepper
      ½  teaspoon crushed red pepper
      ¼  teaspoon oregano leaves
      ¼  teaspoon thyme leaves
      3  dashes hot red pepper sauce
      5  cups hot cooked rice, long-grain brown or
         white

1. Wash ham hocks and place in a large saucepan. Add 1 quart water and bring to a boil. Cover, reduce heat, and simmer 30 minutes or until meat is tender. Remove ham hocks and discard. Strain broth and chill overnight or until fat rises to the surface and hardens. Remove the fat and discard; set broth aside.
2. Sort and wash beans; place in a Dutch oven. Cover with water and soak overnight.
3. Drain beans; combine beans and broth in Dutch oven. Cover and cook over low heat for 45 minutes. Add remaining ingredients except rice; cover and cook over low heat 2–2½ hours, stirring occasionally and adding additional water, if desired. Serve over rice.

*Yield: 10 1-cup servings*

| Nutritive values per 1-cup serving: | CAL | CHO (gm) | PRO (gm) | FAT (gm) |
|---|---|---|---|---|
| | 283 | 49 | 17 | 2 |

Food exchanges per 1-cup serving:

3 BREAD, 1 lean MEAT, 1 VEGETABLE

# Rice and Vegetable Casserole

*Serve this with a green vegetable like steamed fresh green beans and baked chicken or fish. The combination of corn and rice makes this dish a complete protein.*

4 small zucchini, chopped
6 green onions, chopped
1 cup fresh or frozen corn kernels
1 16-ounce can tomatoes, undrained and chopped
½ teaspoon freshly ground pepper
Pinch each basil and thyme leaves
2 cups cooked long-grain brown rice

1. In a large skillet, place first 4 ingredients over medium heat and cook until they begin to boil. Reduce heat and simmer for 10 minutes, until tender and most of the liquid is gone.
2. Stir in the seasonings and rice. Heat for a few minutes.

*Yield: 6 ¾-cup servings*

| Nutritive values per ¾-cup serving: | CAL | CHO (gm) | PRO (gm) | FAT (gm) |
|---|---|---|---|---|
| | 104 | 22 | 4 | 0 |

Food exchanges per ¾-cup serving:

1 BREAD, 1½ VEGETABLE

# Bulgur Pilaf

*Bulgur is cracked wheat. It is parboiled and then cracked into small pieces. It comes in three sizes: the largest for pilaf, the middle-sized for cereal, and the smallest for tabbouli, a Middle Eastern salad. It has a nutty flavor and is very dense, which means it has more calories than the same size serving of some other grains. At the same time, it has lots of fiber and is very filling.*

*For children used to instant rice (or "mush," as I call it), bulgur will be a shock. Try breaking them in slowly. Mix white rice and brown long-grain rice for a while. Then sneak in a little bulgur until your children get used to the brown kernels they need to chew!*

> 2 teaspoons diet margarine
> 1 small onion, minced
> 1 cup bulgur
> 2 cups boiling homemade chicken stock or water
> ¼ teaspoon freshly ground pepper

1. Melt margarine in a medium saucepan. Sauté onion for 5 minutes. Add bulgur and cook for another 2 minutes.
2. Add stock and pepper. Stir. Cover and reduce heat to simmer for 15 minutes or until liquid is absorbed.

*Yield: 6 ⅓-cup servings*

| Nutritive values per ⅓-cup serving: | CAL | CHO (gm) | PRO (gm) | FAT (gm) |
|---|---|---|---|---|
| | 132 | 29 | 4 | 0 |

Food exchanges per ⅓-cup serving:        2 BREAD

# Oven "French Fries"

2 large potatoes
1 tablespoon olive oil
¼ teaspoon salt
¼ teaspoon freshly ground pepper
⅛ teaspoon paprika

1. Preheat oven to 350°F.
2. Cut potatoes into thin strips, leaving the skins on. In a medium bowl, sprinkle remaining ingredients over potatoes and toss thoroughly to coat.
3. Arrange potatoes on a nonstick baking sheet. Bake for 20 minutes. Using spatula, turn potatoes over. Bake 20 minutes longer, until browned and crisp.

*Yield: 4 4-ounce servings*

| Nutritive values per 4-ounce serving: | CAL | CHO (gm) | PRO (gm) | FAT (gm) |
|---|---|---|---|---|
| | 111 | 19 | 3 | 3 |

Food exchanges per 4-ounce
serving:                          1 BREAD, ½ FAT

# Potato-Bean Patties

*This recipe is reproduced completely from* Jane Brody's Good Food Book.

*"Even children who would otherwise never touch a bean devoured these soft croquettes, which have a crisp outer shell. They are excellent as a lunch or supper entree, accompanied by a green vegetable and salad. If you have precooked the beans, the patties can be prepared quickly. Adzuki (or aduki) beans are very small and kidney-red; they are widely available in natural food stores. The closest substitute would be small red beans. For added nutrients and flavor, use the potato water as part of the liquid for cooking the beans. The "batter" or patties can be fully prepared even a day ahead and refrigerated. Because the patties are soft, it is important to fry them with enough space between them so that they can be turned easily. They are easier to handle on a pancake griddle (preferably one with a nonstick surface) rather than a frying pan."*

    1  pound unpeeled potatoes, scrubbed and
       boiled in lightly salted water until tender
    1  egg white
    3  tablespoons skim milk
    1  teaspoon butter or margarine
       Freshly ground black pepper to taste
    2  tablespoons minced fresh parsley
    ½  cup dried adzuki beans, soaked and
       cooked until tender but not mushy
    ½  cup grated Parmesan cheese
  2–3  tablespoons vegetable oil

1. When the potatoes are cool enough to handle, peel and mash them with egg white, milk, butter or margarine, and pepper.
2. Stir in the parsley and fold in the cooked beans.
3. Form the mixture into 16 patties (about 2½ inches in diameter), coating each one on both sides with the grated cheese. Place them on a flat surface on a sheet

of wax paper, but do not let them touch.

**4.** In batches on an oiled griddle or in a skillet, fry the patties until they are browned on both sides, taking care when turning them not to mush them. Keep the cooked patties warm in the oven until serving time.

*Yield: 8 servings (2 patties each)*

| Nutritive values per 2-patty serving: | CAL | CHO (gm) | PRO (gm) | FAT (gm) |
|---|---|---|---|---|
| | 133 | 16 | 6 | 5 |

| Food exchanges per 2-patty serving: | 1 BREAD, 1 medium-fat MEAT |
|---|---|

# Potato Kugel

*This is a recipe from my vegetarian friend, Wendy Iscov, who is also the mother of two boys.*

5 medium potatoes, grated coarse
2 medium onions, chopped
2 eggs, beaten
2 cloves garlic, minced
1 teaspoon freshly ground pepper
1 teaspoon salt
3 tablespoons matzo meal

**1.** Preheat oven to 350°F.

**2.** Mix all ingredients completely. Pour into an oiled 9- by 13-inch baking dish. Bake for 1½ hours. Cut into 10 equal portions.

*Yield: 10 ½-cup servings*

| Nutritive values per ½-cup serving: | CAL | CHO (gm) | PRO (gm) | FAT (gm) |
|---|---|---|---|---|
| | 97 | 18 | 4 | 1 |

| Food exchanges per ½-cup serving: | 1 BREAD, trace FAT |
|---|---|

# Stuffed Yams

*Yams have a good glycemic index rating. They raise blood sugar at a much slower rate and to a lower level than white potatoes.*

> 2 medium yams (about 1½ pounds), scrubbed and baked
> ½ cup unsweetened, undrained crushed pineapple
> ¼ teaspoon ground cinnamon
> ¼ teaspoon ground nutmeg

1. Preheat oven to 400°F.
2. Cut each baked yam in half lengthwise. Scoop pulp into bowl, leaving shells intact.
3. Mash pulp with other ingredients. Spoon one-quarter of mixture into each shell. Bake about 15 minutes.

*Yield: 4 ½-cup servings*

| Nutritive values per ½-cup serving: | CAL | CHO (gm) | PRO (gm) | FAT (gm) |
|---|---|---|---|---|
| | 152 | 34 | 4 | 0 |

Food exchanges per ½-cup serving:     2 BREAD, ½ FRUIT

# Puffed Sweet Potatoes

*Like yams, sweet potatoes have good glycemic index ratings.*

2 medium sweet potatoes, baked
¼ cup unsweetened orange juice
¼ teaspoon ground ginger
¼ teaspoon ground nutmeg
1 teaspoon grated orange zest
2 egg whites

1. Preheat oven to 350°F.
2. Peel sweet potatoes and mash pulp. Add juice, ginger, nutmeg, and grated zest.
3. Beat egg whites until stiff peaks form and fold them into sweet potato mixture. Spoon into a 1-quart non-stick baking dish and bake for 30 minutes.

*Yield: 4 ½-cup servings*

| Nutritive values per ½-cup serving: | CAL | CHO (gm) | PRO (gm) | FAT (gm) |
|---|---|---|---|---|
| | 116 | 31 | 5 | 0 |

| Food exchanges per ½-cup serving: | 2 BREAD |
|---|---|

# Sweet Potatoes and Bananas

*I had this at my friend Bette Mazur's house. I took out the butter and sugar, and it's still great.*

> 2 pounds sweet potatoes or yams, cooked and peeled
> 3 bananas, peeled and sliced
> ½ cup unsweetened orange juice
> 4 packets artificial sweetener (equal to 8 teaspoons sugar)
> ½ teaspoon ground cinnamon
> ¼ teaspoon ground nutmeg

**1.** Preheat oven to 375°F.
**2.** Slice potatoes. Toss bananas with ¼ cup orange juice.
**3.** In 2-quart baking dish, layer half the potatoes, then ⅔ of the sliced bananas. Mix the sweetener, cinnamon, and nutmeg and sprinkle half over the potatoes and bananas. Pour in any juice left over from tossing the bananas. Layer remaining potatoes; end with remaining bananas in the center. Pour remaining orange juice over and sprinkle with sweetener mixture.
**4.** Bake for 45 minutes, until bubbly.

*Yield: 6 ⅔-cup servings*

| Nutritive values per ⅔-cup serving: | CAL | CHO (gm) | PRO (gm) | FAT (gm) |
|---|---|---|---|---|
| | 112 | 25 | 3 | 0 |

Food exchanges per ⅔-cup
serving:                            1 BREAD, 1 FRUIT

# STARCHY VEGETABLES
## Carrot-Acorn Squash

*I could never get my younger son to eat acorn squash until I served it like this.*

>2 acorn squash (approximately 1½ pounds each)
>2 cups cooked sliced carrots
>1 tablespoon fresh lemon juice
>¼ teaspoon each ground nutmeg and mace
>1 tablespoon grated orange zest

**1.** Preheat oven to 350°F.
**2.** Cut squash in half lengthwise and remove seeds. Place cut side down on baking sheet and bake for 40–45 minutes, until tender.
**3.** Scoop out squash pulp. Put squash and carrots, juice, spices, and zest in blender or food processor. Whirl briefly. Don't let it turn to complete mush, or you lose the value of the fiber in the vegetables. Serve warm.

**Variation**
The quickest version of the recipe above is to make it without the carrots. Put the squash pulp in the blender or processor with ⅛ teaspoon nutmeg, ⅛ teaspoon mace, and 1 tablespoon orange zest.

*Yield: 6 ¾-cup servings*

| | CAL | CHO (gm) | PRO (gm) | FAT (gm) |
|---|---|---|---|---|
| Nutritive values per ¾-cup serving: | 92 | 20 | 3 | 0 |
| Food exchanges per ¾-cup serving: | 1 BREAD, 1 VEGETABLE | | | |

| | CAL | CHO (gm) | PRO (gm) | FAT (gm) |
|---|---|---|---|---|
| Nutritive values Variation per serving: | 72 | 16 | 3 | 0 |
| Food exchanges Variation per serving: | 1 BREAD | | | |

# Corn Pudding

*This is wonderful served with anything. It's even good for breakfast. The milk, eggs, and corn provide complete protein with some fiber. You can use diet margarine, but the taste will be a little different. I use the butter and balance it by serving it with other very low-fat dishes.*

> 3 tablespoons butter, softened, or diet margarine
> 3 packets artificial sweetener (equal to 2 tablespoons sugar)
> 2 tablespoons unbleached white flour
> ½ teaspoon salt
> 2 whole eggs
> 3 egg whites
> 2 cups fresh corn kernels *or* 1 10-ounce bag frozen corn kernels
> 1⅓ cups evaporated skim milk
> ½ teaspoon ground cumin (optional)

**1.** Preheat oven to 325°F.
**2.** Blend butter, sweetener, flour, and salt.
**3.** Add eggs and egg whites and beat well. Stir in corn, milk, and cumin, if desired. Mix well. Pour into oiled 2-quart baking dish and bake for 45 minutes. Stir only once during baking. When done, it will be golden brown and of custard consistency. Knife inserted half-way between side and center should come out clean.

*Yield: 6 ¾-cup servings*

| Nutritive values per ¾-cup serving: | CAL | CHO (gm) | PRO (gm) | FAT (gm) |
|---|---|---|---|---|
| | 157 | 18 | 10 | 5 |

| Food exchanges per ¾-cup serving: | 1 BREAD, ½ MILK, ½ lean MEAT, 1 FAT |
|---|---|

# Squash with Apples

1 pound winter squash (acorn, butternut, or Hubbard), peeled and seeded
1 large baking apple, peeled
¼ cup water
1 tablespoon diet margarine
1 tablespoon fresh lemon juice
1 tablespoon molasses
4 packets artificial sweetener (Equal)
¼ teaspoon ground cinnamon
⅛ teaspoon ground nutmeg

**1.** Cut squash and apple into ½-inch cubes.
**2.** Put squash and apple into large skillet with water, margarine, and lemon juice over medium-high heat. Cover and cook, stirring occasionally, until just tender and liquid is absorbed.
**3.** Stir in molasses, sweetener, and spices.

*Yield: 4 ½-cup servings*

| Nutritive values per ½-cup serving: | CAL | CHO (gm) | PRO (gm) | FAT (gm) |
|---|---|---|---|---|
| | 109 | 24 | 1 | 1 |

Food exchanges per ½-cup serving:          1 BREAD, 1 FRUIT, trace FAT

# Oven-Fried Squash

½ cup cornmeal
½ teaspoon salt
¼ teaspoon freshly ground pepper
1 egg
3 tablespoons nonfat yogurt
3 medium yellow squash or zucchini, cut
  into ¼-inch slices
  Lemon wedges

1. Preheat oven to 350°F.
2. Combine cornmeal, salt, and pepper; set aside. Combine egg and yogurt; beat well. Dip squash in egg mixture; dredge in cornmeal.
3. Place squash in a nonstick baking pan in a single layer. Bake for 30–40 minutes, until golden, turning once. Serve with lemon wedges.

*Yield: 6 ⅓-cup servings*

| Nutritive values per ⅓-cup serving: | CAL | CHO (gm) | PRO (gm) | FAT (gm) |
|---|---|---|---|---|
| | 69 | 12 | 3 | 1 |

Food exchanges per ⅓-cup serving:

½ BREAD, 1 VEGETABLE, trace FAT

# NONSTARCHY VEGETABLES

# Cauliflower or Broccoli Parmesan

*Here's an easy way to add some zest to these vegetables.*

1 pound broccoli or cauliflower
2 tablespoons water for microwave *or* ¼ cup
  water for steaming
1 tablespoon diet margarine, melted
  Juice of ½ lemon
2 tablespoons minced fresh parsley
  Freshly ground white pepper
2 tablespoons grated Parmesan cheese

**1.** Cut tough stem ends off broccoli. Cut into long-stemmed flowerets (they look like trees to some children). Do the same for cauliflower (only shorter!).

**2.** For microwaving, put vegetables into 1-quart casserole with 2 tablespoons water and cover with plastic. Cook on HIGH for 5 minutes. Let stand for 3–4 minutes. Test with fork to see if it's tender. Broccoli should still be bright green. For steaming, place ¼ cup water in saucepan. Bring to boil. Use a steamer basket if you have one. Cover and steam for 5 minutes. Let stand, covered, for 3–4 minutes.

**3.** Drizzle margarine over vegetables in a serving dish. Squeeze lemon over and top with parsley, pepper, and cheese. Serve.

*Yield: 4 ¾-cup servings*

| Nutritive values per ¾-cup serving: | CAL | CHO (gm) | PRO (gm) | FAT (gm) |
|---|---|---|---|---|
| | 54 | 6 | 3 | 2 |
| Food exchanges per ¾-cup serving: | 1 VEGETABLE, ½ FAT | | | |

# Sesame Broccoli

*I prepare broccoli at least once a week. It's one of the most nutritious vegetables you can eat. Broccoli is a member of the cabbage family. Cabbage family members also include cauliflower, Brussels sprouts, kale, turnip greens, and kohlrabi. They contain substances called indoles that help protect cells from damage by cancer-causing chemicals. Broccoli is also an excellent source of vitamin C, vitamin A, and fiber.*

    1  1½-pound bunch broccoli
    ½  teaspoon sesame oil
    1  tablespoon sesame seeds
    1  teaspoon peanut oil
    1  clove garlic, minced
    6  green onions, chopped
    ½  cup sliced water chestnuts (optional)
    1  tablespoon dry sherry
    1  tablespoon soy sauce
    2  tablespoons water

1. Trim leaves off broccoli. Remove tough ends of lower stalks. Cut into flowerets and cut peeled stem into ¼-inch slices.
2. Heat sesame oil in wok or large skillet until hot. Toast sesame seeds until they start to turn golden. Remove and set aside.
3. Add peanut oil to wok with garlic and onions. Stir-fry for 1 minute.
4. Add broccoli slices and stir-fry for 3 minutes. Add flowerets and remaining ingredients. Reduce heat, cover, and steam for 5 minutes. Sprinkle sesame seeds over and serve.

**Variation**
Add 3 medium carrots, sliced, with broccoli slices and ¼ head green cabbage, chopped, with flowerets.

*Yield: 6 ¾-cup servings*

| Nutritive values per ¾-cup serving: | | CHO | PRO | FAT |
|---|---|---|---|---|
| | CAL | (gm) | (gm) | (gm) |
| | 71 | 8 | 3 | 3 |

| Food exchanges per ¾-cup serving: | 1½ VEGETABLE, ½ FAT |
|---|---|

| Nutritive values Variation per ¾-cup serving: | | CHO | PRO | FAT |
|---|---|---|---|---|
| | CAL | (gm) | (gm) | (gm) |
| | 96 | 13 | 5 | 3 |

| Food exchanges Variation per ¾-cup serving: | 2½ VEGETABLE, ½ FAT |
|---|---|

# Tart Red Cabbage

*This can be served hot or cold.*

½ cup red wine
½ cup red wine vinegar
½ teaspoon ground cinnamon
1 small onion, chopped
1 small head red cabbage (about 1–1½ pounds), shredded
2 medium apples, sliced thin

Combine wine, vinegar, and cinnamon in large, heavy saucepan. Heat to boil and reduce heat. Add onion, cabbage, and apples. Simmer for 1½ hours, covered. Add a little water if necessary.

*Yield: 6 ½-cup servings*

| Nutritive values per ½-cup serving: | | CHO | PRO | FAT |
|---|---|---|---|---|
| | CAL | (gm) | (gm) | (gm) |
| | 68 | 15 | 2 | 0 |

| Food exchanges per ½-cup serving: | 1 FRUIT, 1 VEGETABLE |
|---|---|

# Sautéed Cabbage

*Cabbage is rich in fiber, potassium, and vitamin C. Add shredded red or green cabbage to salads for extra nutrition.*

1   1½-pound head green cabbage
1   shallot, minced, *or* ¼ small onion, minced
1   tablespoon minced fresh parsley
    Freshly ground pepper to taste
½   cup homemade chicken stock
½   teaspoon fennel seeds

1. With a sharp knife, cut out most of the core of the cabbage, leaving just enough to hold the head together. Slice the head into wedges about 1½ inches thick.
2. Put the cabbage, shallot, parsley, pepper, and stock in a large skillet. Cover and cook the cabbage over moderate heat for about 12 minutes, basting it several times with the pan juices.
3. When the cabbage is nearly done, sprinkle it with fennel seeds. Serve the cabbage with a little of the pan juices.

*Yield: 6 ½-cup servings*

| Nutritive values per ½-cup serving: | CAL | CHO (gm) | PRO (gm) | FAT (gm) |
|---|---|---|---|---|
| | 28 | 5 | 2 | 0 |

| Food exchanges per ½-cup serving: | |
|---|---|
| | 1 VEGETABLE |

# Fruit Spiced Carrots

1 pound carrots, without tops
¼ cup water
½ cup unsweetened orange or pineapple juice
½ teaspoon ground cinnamon
¼ teaspoon ground nutmeg
1 teaspoon grated orange or lemon zest

**1.** Cut carrots into ¼-inch slices. Combine water and juice with carrots in a medium saucepan. Bring to a boil. Cover and simmer for 20 minutes, until tender.
**2.** Stir in spices and zest.

**Variation**
Cook carrots in water and drain. Sprinkle with 1 tablespoon diet margarine, melted, juice of ½ lemon, and 1 packet Equal. Stir and serve.

*Yield: 8 ½-cup servings*

| Nutritive values per ½-cup serving: | CAL | CHO (gm) | PRO (gm) | FAT (gm) |
|---|---|---|---|---|
| | 28 | 5 | 2 | 0 |

| Food exchanges per ½-cup serving: | 1 VEGETABLE |
|---|---|

# Cucumber Salad

        4  cucumbers, peeled and sliced
        4  green onions, chopped
        ¼  cup chopped fresh parsley
        1  teaspoon dried dillweed
        ½  teaspoon basil leaves
        1  clove garlic, minced or pressed
        1  tablespoon dark sesame oil
        ½  cup rice vinegar

Put all ingredients into a bowl. Mix lightly and refrigerate
2–3 hours before serving.

*Yield: 8 ½-cup servings*

| Nutritive values per ½-cup serving: | CAL | CHO (gm) | PRO (gm) | FAT (gm) |
|---|---|---|---|---|
| | 21 | 3 | 0 | 1 |

Food exchanges per ½-cup
serving:　　　　　　　　　　　½ VEGETABLE, trace FAT


# Continental Green Beans

*I love green beans raw, and my boys will sometimes eat
them with dip. You can steam them for 5 minutes (they
should still be bright green) or try this easy recipe.*

        1  16-ounce bag frozen green beans,
           defrosted, *or* 1 pound fresh, trimmed
        1  6-ounce can tomato juice
        ½  small onion, minced
        1  teaspoon oregano leaves
        ¼  teaspoon freshly ground pepper
        1  tablespoon grated Parmesan cheese

Combine all ingredients except cheese in a saucepan.
Simmer, covered, for 3 minutes. Uncover and simmer
until liquid is almost gone. Sprinkle with cheese.

*Yield: 4 ½-cup servings*

| Nutritive values per ½-cup serving: | | CHO (gm) | PRO (gm) | FAT (gm) |
|---|---|---|---|---|
| | CAL | | | |
| | 48 | 9 | 3 | 0 |

Food exchanges per ½-cup serving:                    2 VEGETABLE

# Baked Spinach

*This recipe is an adaptation of one I found in* The Art of Cooking for the Diabetic, *by Katharine Middleton and Mary Abbott Hess (Contemporary Books, 1978).*

- 2 eggs, beaten
- 1 tablespoon flour
- ¼ teaspoon salt
- ⅛ teaspoon freshly ground pepper
- 1 small clove garlic, minced
- ½ teaspoon ground nutmeg
- 1 tablespoon fresh lemon juice
- 2 10-ounce packages frozen chopped spinach, defrosted
- ½ teaspoon olive oil

1. Preheat oven to 350°F.
2. Beat eggs and add flour, salt, pepper, garlic, nutmeg, and lemon juice. Beat well. Add spinach and mix.
3. Oil 1-quart casserole with olive oil. Pour mixture in and bake for 20–25 minutes.

*Yield: 5 ½-cup servings*

| Nutritive values per ½-cup serving: | | CHO (gm) | PRO (gm) | FAT (gm) |
|---|---|---|---|---|
| | CAL | | | |
| | 54 | 5 | 4 | 2 |

Food exchanges per ½-cup serving:                1 VEGETABLE, ½ FAT

# Stir-Fry Squash

1 pound yellow squash or zucchini
2 teaspoons peanut oil
2 green onions, sliced
1 teaspoon soy sauce
1 teaspoon sugar
2 tablespoons water

1. Cut squash in half lengthwise, then diagonally into ¼-inch slices.
2. Heat peanut oil in a wok or heavy skillet over high heat. Add onions and stir-fry for a few seconds. Add squash and cook, stirring, for 1 minute.
3. Add soy sauce, sugar, and water. Stir well. Cover and cook over medium heat for 3 minutes. Serve.

*Yield: 4 ⅔-cup servings*

| Nutritive values per ⅔-cup serving: | CAL | CHO (gm) | PRO (gm) | FAT (gm) |
|---|---|---|---|---|
| | 50 | 6 | 2 | 2 |

Food exchanges per ⅔-cup serving:                1 VEGETABLE, ½ FAT

# Zucchini Italiano

3 cups sliced zucchini (approximately 1 pound)
1 cup homemade chicken broth
1 6-ounce can tomato paste
1 onion, chopped
1 teaspoon oregano leaves
1 teaspoon basil leaves
1 clove garlic, minced
1 tablespoon bread crumbs
2 tablespoons grated Parmesan cheese

1. Preheat oven to 350°F.
2. Combine zucchini, broth, tomato paste, onion, herbs, and garlic in casserole. Sprinkle with crumbs and cheese. Bake, uncovered, for 1 hour or until tender.

*Yield: 6 ½-cup servings*

| Nutritive values per ½-cup serving: | CAL | CHO (gm) | PRO (gm) | FAT (gm) |
|---|---|---|---|---|
| | 48 | 9 | 3 | 0 |

Food exchanges per ½-cup serving:                    2 VEGETABLE

# Swiss Chard Sauté

*This is a tasty way to prepare this healthy green. If your child won't eat it, eat it yourself and make a fuss about how good it is! Both Swiss chard and kale are rich in calcium and vitamins A and C.*

> 1 teaspoon sesame oil or olive oil
> 1 teaspoon minced garlic
> ½ cup thinly sliced onion
> ⅔ cup sliced celery
> 1 tablespoon water
> 4 cups coarsely chopped Swiss chard or kale
>     Freshly ground black pepper
> 1 tablespoon red wine vinegar

**1.** Heat the oil in a large skillet (preferably nonstick) and add the garlic, onion, and celery. Sauté, stirring, for about 3 minutes

**2.** Add the water and the Swiss chard. Season the mixture with pepper, stirring the ingredients to combine them well. Cover the pan and simmer the mixture, stirring it occasionally, over low heat for about 5 minutes or until the chard is wilted and tender. Sprinkle vinegar over the mixture.

*Yield: 4 ½-cup servings*

| | CAL | CHO (gm) | PRO (gm) | FAT (gm) |
|---|---|---|---|---|
| Nutritive values per ½-cup serving: | 62 | 8 | 3 | 2 |

Food exchanges per ½-cup serving:      1½ VEGETABLE, ½ FAT

# Mashed Turnips

*These two recipes are good ways to prepare turnips that children will enjoy because they masquerade as potatoes!*

1 pound turnips, peeled and diced
2 cups boiling water
1 tablespoon diet margarine
½ teaspoon salt
¼ teaspoon freshly ground pepper
¼ teaspoon ground nutmeg
  Paprika

1. Add turnips to boiling water in a saucepan. Lower heat, cover, and cook 20 minutes, until tender. Drain.
2. Mash turnips, adding margarine and seasonings. Sprinkle some paprika on top.

*Yield: 4 ½-cup servings*

| Nutritive values per ½-cup serving: | CAL | CHO (gm) | PRO (gm) | FAT (gm) |
|---|---|---|---|---|
| | 41 | 7 | 1 | 1 |

Food exchanges per ½-cup serving:                   1½ VEGETABLE

# Hash Brown Turnips

1 pound turnips, peeled and diced
1 teaspoon olive oil
½ cup chopped onion
¼ teaspoon salt
¼ teaspoon freshly ground pepper
¼ teaspoon powdered sage
¼ teaspoon thyme leaves

1. Cook turnips in a covered saucepan in boiling water to cover, about 20 minutes, until tender. Drain.
2. Heat oil in skillet over medium-high heat. Add all ingredients and cook, stirring occasionally, until turnips are lightly browned.

*Yield: 4 ½-cup servings*

| Nutritive values per ½-cup serving: | CAL | CHO (gm) | PRO (gm) | FAT (gm) |
|---|---|---|---|---|
| | 49 | 8 | 2 | 1 |

| Food exchanges per ½-cup serving: | 1½ VEGETABLE |
|---|---|

# Chinese Vegetables

*I serve this with the Oriental Flank Steak earlier in this chapter (see index for recipe). It's one of my boys' favorite dinners. Bok choy looks like a cross between celery and spinach and is available in many large supermarkets. It is a good source of calcium and vitamin A. It is a member of the cabbage family and contains cancer-blocking agents.*

      1  teaspoon dark sesame oil
      1  clove garlic, minced
      1  teaspoon seeded and minced fresh
         gingerroot
      2  stalks celery, chopped
      4  green onions, chopped
      1  green pepper, cut into strips
      6  water chestnuts, sliced
     ½  pound fresh Chinese pea pods, stemmed
      1  bunch bok choy, cut across the stalk in
         shreds
      2  teaspoons soy sauce
      2  tablespoons cream sherry
      2  tablespoons chicken stock or water

**1.** Heat oil in wok or large skillet and stir-fry garlic and ginger over medium-high heat for 1 minute.

**2.** Add remaining ingredients, turn heat to high, and stir-fry for 3–4 minutes. Turn heat off, cover, and let steam for 2 minutes. Serve.

**Variation**

Use ½ head green cabbage, shredded, instead of bok choy, and 2 small zucchini instead of celery, cut into julienne strips. Add 1 medium tomato, chopped. (No real difference in exchanges.)

*Yield: 6 ¾-cup servings*

| Nutritive values per serving: | CAL | CHO (gm) | PRO (gm) | FAT (gm) |
|---|---|---|---|---|
|  | 44 | 8 | 3 | 0 |
| Food exchanges per serving: | 1½ VEGETABLE | | | |

# Skillet Vegetables

*This recipe is great served many different ways. Serve it over brown rice for a complete meal, or add extra chili powder and serve it on a flour tortilla, or serve it as is, for a tasty vegetable side dish.*

1 large onion, chopped
1 clove garlic, minced
3 small zucchini, sliced
3 carrots, sliced thin
2 stalks celery, sliced thin
1 cup broccoli flowerets
1 cup cauliflower pieces
1 cup frozen corn kernels
1 16-ounce can tomatoes
1 teaspoon basil leaves
1 teaspoon chili powder
1 cup shredded sharp cheddar cheese

1. Place all vegetables in large, heavy skillet, breaking up tomatoes into small pieces.
2. Add seasonings. Cover and simmer for 45 minutes to 1 hour, until tender. Put cheese on top, cover, and cook until cheese melts, 2–3 minutes.

*Yield: 8 ⅔-cup servings*

| Nutritive values per ⅔-cup serving: | CAL | CHO (gm) | PRO (gm) | FAT (gm) |
|---|---|---|---|---|
| | 117 | 11 | 7 | 5 |

Food exchanges per ⅔-cup serving:          ½ high-fat MEAT, 2 VEGETABLE

# BREAD

I usually don't serve bread with dinner. My children eat bread with breakfast and lunch. I feel dinner is a good time to add more variety to their daily nutrition by serving starchy vegetables. Popovers are one exception because they seem like a treat to my boys. We serve them on special occasions. Irish Soda Bread (see index) is also a good choice.

## Popovers

*This classic recipe calls for a little lemon or orange zest for extra zing. For high, puffed-up popovers, heat the muffin pans or custard cups before you pour in the batter.*

    1  teaspoon oil
    2  medium eggs, slightly beaten
    1  cup whole milk
    1  cup sifted unbleached white flour
    ½  teaspoon salt
    1  tablespoon melted butter or diet margarine
    ½  teaspoon grated orange or lemon zest

1. Preheat oven to 450°F.
2. Oil 8 2½-inch muffin cups or 8 custard cups and set aside.
3. Combine eggs, milk, flour, and salt and beat until smooth, a few minutes. Add butter or margarine. Beat another 30 seconds. Add zest.
4. Pour batter into custard cups or muffin cups. Bake 15 minutes, then reduce heat to 350°F and bake for another 20 minutes, until firm and browned. You can pierce the popovers with a sharp knife to let the steam escape.

*Yield: 8 popovers*

| Nutritive values per serving: | CAL | CHO (gm) | PRO (gm) | FAT (gm) |
|---|---|---|---|---|
| | 108 | 12 | 4 | 4 |
| Food exchanges per serving: | 1 BREAD, 1 FAT | | | |

222 KIDS, FOOD, AND DIABETES

# SALAD DRESSINGS AND GRAVY
## No-Calorie Dressing

*This dressing is based on one I saw in* The Art of Cooking for the Diabetic, *by Katharine Middleton and Mary Abbott Hess (Contemporary Books, 1978).*

½ cup fresh lemon juice or white or red wine vinegar
¼ cup water
1 tablespoon minced fresh parsley
½ teaspoon dried dillweed
1 teaspoon grated lemon zest
½ teaspoon Worcestershire sauce
¼ teaspoon celery seeds
¼ teaspoon pepper
¼ teaspoon dry mustard
2 packets artificial sweetener (Equal) (only if you use the lemon juice)

Blend all ingredients together.

*Yield: ¾ cup*

| Nutritive values per 2-tablespoon serving: | CAL | CHO (gm) | PRO (gm) | FAT (gm) |
|---|---|---|---|---|
| | 4 | 1 | 0 | 0 |

Food exchanges per 2-tablespoon serving:  FREE up to ½ cup

# Tangy Buttermilk Dressing

*This is similar to ranch-style dressing, but it's a free food!*

¾ cup buttermilk (from skim milk)
1 tablespoon prepared horseradish (no added sugar)
1 tablespoon fresh lemon juice
1 packet artificial sweetener (Equal)
1 tablespoon Dijon mustard
1 teaspoon dried dillweed
2 tablespoons minced fresh parsley

Blend all ingredients together.

*Yield: 1 cup*

| Nutritive values per 2-tablespoon serving: | CAL | CHO (gm) | PRO (gm) | FAT (gm) |
|---|---|---|---|---|
| | 8 | 1 | 1 | 0 |

Food exchanges per 2-tablespoon serving:

FREE up to ⅓ cup

# Mock Thousand Island Dressing

¼ cup nonfat yogurt
¼ cup catsup or chili sauce
2 tablespoons wine vinegar or fresh lemon juice
Freshly ground pepper to taste
⅛ teaspoon hot red pepper sauce
⅛ teaspoon garlic powder
½ teaspoon Worcestershire sauce

**1.** Combine all ingredients well.
**2.** Chill before serving on tossed greens.

*Yield: ½ cup (4 servings)*

| Nutritive values per 2-tablespoon serving: | CAL | CHO (gm) | PRO (gm) | FAT (gm) |
|---|---|---|---|---|
| | 24 | 6 | 0 | 0 |

Food exchanges per 2-tablespoon serving:  ½ BREAD

# Creamy Vinaigrette

*This is from* Jane Brody's Good Food Book.

⅔ cup low-fat yogurt
⅓ cup apple cider vinegar
2 tablespoons olive oil
1 tablespoon Dijon mustard
1 tablespoon fresh lemon juice
1 very large clove garlic, crushed
1 tablespoon reduced-sodium soy sauce
(optional)
¼ teaspoon dried dillweed

Combine all ingredients in a bowl or jar with a tight-fitting lid. Whisk or shake to blend well.

*Yield: about 1¼ cups*

| Nutritive values per 2-tablespoon serving: | CAL | CHO (gm) | PRO (gm) | FAT (gm) |
|---|---|---|---|---|
| | 35 | 1 | 1 | 3 |

Food exchanges per 2-tablespoon
serving:                            ½ FAT

# Low-Calorie Mayonnaise

1 cup low-fat cottage cheese or part-skim
  ricotta
2 tablespoons fresh lemon juice
2 egg yolks
1 teaspoon Dijon mustard
1 teaspoon dillweed or basil or chives
  (optional)
¼ teaspoon salt

Blend all ingredients in a blender or food processor until
they are smooth.

*Yield: 1⅓ cup*

| Nutritive values per 1-tablespoon serving: | CAL | CHO (gm) | PRO (gm) | FAT (gm) |
|---|---|---|---|---|
| | 61 | 0 | 4 | 5 |

| Food exchanges per 1-tablespoon serving: | ½ lean MEAT, ½ FAT |
|---|---|

# Gravy from Meat Drippings

*Here's a low-calorie, low-fat gravy for your whole family.*

Skim milk, bouillon, water, or vegetable
stock
Meat drippings with fat removed*
2 tablespoons flour
¼ cup cold skim milk, bouillon, water, or
vegetable stock
Salt and pepper to taste

**1.** Add liquid to the drippings to make a total of ¾ cup.
**2.** Mix the flour with ¼ cup cold liquid.
**3.** Stir flour mixture into drippings mixture.
**4.** Heat, stirring constantly, until thickened.
**5.** Season to taste with salt and pepper.

*Yield: 1 cup*

| Nutritive values per ¼-cup serving: | CAL | CHO (gm) | PRO (gm) | FAT (gm) |
|---|---|---|---|---|
| | 16 | 4 | 0 | 0 |

| Food exchanges per ¼-cup serving: | FREE |
|---|---|

---

*To remove fat from drippings, pour drippings into a container. Chill in refrigerator (may be chilled quickly by putting in the freezer or adding an ice cube to the drippings). Remove solid fat that forms at the top. Store extra drippings in refrigerator or freezer for later use.

# DESSERTS
## Lemon Snow Pudding

*Here's a free dessert! It's courtesy of* The Art of Cooking for the Diabetic, *by Katharine Middleton and Mary Abbott Hess (Contemporary Books, 1978).*

1 tablespoon unflavored granulated gelatin
½ cup cold water
1 tablespoon grated lemon zest
¼ cup fresh lemon juice
1¼ cups boiling water
12 packets artificial sweetener (Equal)
2 medium egg whites
¼ teaspoon vanilla extract
¼ teaspoon lemon extract
Grated lemon zest for garnish

1. Soak gelatin in cold water. Meanwhile, combine lemon zest, juice, and boiling water in a bowl. Add softened gelatin and sweetener; mix well. Chill until it is the consistency of unbeaten egg whites.
2. Add unbeaten egg whites, vanilla extract, and lemon extract. Beat with a rotary beater until it is very fluffy and holds its shape. Pile into 6 parfait glasses. Top with a little extra grated lemon zest.

*Yield: 4 ½-cup servings*

---

| | |
|---|---|
| Nutritive values per serving: | This whole recipe is 32 calories and not quite 1 lean MEAT |
| Food exchanges per serving: | FREE up to 2 cups |

# Chocolate Delight

1 envelope unflavored gelatin
2 tablespoons unsweetened cocoa powder
2 eggs, separated
2 cups skim milk
1½ teaspoons vanilla extract
12 packets artificial sweetener (Equal)

1. In a medium saucepan, mix unflavored gelatin with cocoa. Beat egg yolks with 1 cup of the skim milk and add to saucepan. Let stand 1 minute.
2. Place saucepan over low heat and stir until gelatin is dissolved, about 5 minutes. Remove from heat. Add remaining cup of skim milk, plus vanilla and sweetener. Chill mixture in a large bowl, stirring occasionally, until slight mounds form when dropped from a spoon.
3. In a large bowl, beat egg whites at high speed until soft peaks form. Gradually add gelatin mixture and beat until mixture increases in volume, about 5 minutes.
4. Chill until slightly thickened. Turn into individual dishes or a 4-cup serving bowl. Chill until firm.

*Yield: 8 ½-cup servings*

| Nutritive values per ½-cup serving: | CAL | CHO (gm) | PRO (gm) | FAT (gm) |
|---|---|---|---|---|
| | 41 | 4 | 4 | 1 |

Food exchanges per ½-cup serving: ½ MILK, trace FAT

# Chocolate Sauce

*This recipe is from* The New Diabetic Cookbook, *by Mabel Cavaiani (Contemporary Books, 1984). It's nice to have an alternative to fudge sauce that's appropriate for diabetics on special occasions.*

3 tablespoons unsweetened cocoa powder
1 tablespoon cornstarch
⅓ cup instant dry milk
⅛ teaspoon salt
1½ cups water
1 tablespoon margarine
2 teaspoons vanilla extract
12 packets artificial sweetener (Equal)

1. Stir together cocoa, cornstarch, dry milk, and salt to blend in a small saucepan. Stir water into dry mixture until smooth. Add margarine and cook and stir over low heat. Bring to a boil and simmer 2 minutes, stirring constantly. Remove from heat.
2. Add vanilla and sweetener to sauce. Stir lightly to mix. Pour into a glass jar and refrigerate until used. Return to room temperature before serving over ice cream or reheat to serve on cake or pudding.

*Yield: 1½ cups (12 servings)*

| Nutritive values per 2-tablespoon serving: | CAL | CHO (gm) | PRO (gm) | FAT (gm) |
|---|---|---|---|---|
| | 29 | 3 | 2 | 1 |

Food exchanges per 2-tablespoon serving: ¼ MILK, trace FAT

# All-American Cranberry Sauce

*The original recipe called for 1½ cups of maple syrup. I played around with it and came up with the following. After you taste it, I doubt you will ever use canned cranberry sauce again!*

    1  12-ounce bag fresh cranberries, sorted and
       washed
    ¼  cup real maple syrup
    1  cup water
    2  teaspoons maple flavoring
    1  tablespoon grated orange zest
    ¾  teaspoon ground ginger
    2  teaspoons arrowroot
    12 packets artificial sweetener (Equal)

**1.** In medium saucepan, combine cranberries, syrup, and water and bring to boil. Reduce heat and simmer for 5 minutes, until berries start to pop.

**2.** Add maple flavoring, orange zest, and ginger. Cook a few minutes. Stir in arrowroot and simmer until thickened. Stir in sweetener. Mix thoroughly. Cool and refrigerate.

*Yield: 2 cups (16 servings)*

| Nutritive values per 2-tablespoon serving: | CAL | CHO (gm) | PRO (gm) | FAT (gm) |
|---|---|---|---|---|
| | 24 | 6 | 0 | 0 |

| Food exchanges per 2-tablespoon serving: | ½ FRUIT |
|---|---|

# Cranberry Relish

1  12-ounce package fresh cranberries,
   washed and drained
1  orange, seeded
1  apple, cored
8  packets artificial sweetener (Equal)

Place a small amount of cranberries, a slice of orange, and a slice of apple in a blender or food processor and chop coarsely. Repeat until all ingredients are chopped. Add sweetener. Mix well and chill overnight.

*Yield: 12 ¼-cup servings*

| Nutritive values per ¼-cup serving: | CAL | CHO (gm) | PRO (gm) | FAT (gm) |
|---|---|---|---|---|
| | 24 | 6 | 0 | 0 |

Food exchanges per ¼-cup
serving:                           ½ FRUIT (up to 4 tablespoons
                                   FREE)

# Cranberry Mold

*This is another adaptation of what is normally a highly caloric recipe.*

  1  12-ounce bag fresh cranberries
  1  orange
  1  3-ounce package sugar-free lemon gelatin
  1  3-ounce package sugar-free raspberry gelatin
  2  cups boiling water
  1  20-ounce can unsweetened crushed pineapple in juice
 ½  cup chopped walnuts
  1  teaspoon peeled and grated fresh gingerroot *or* ½ teaspoon ground ginger
 12  packets artificial sweetener (Equal)

1. Grind cranberries in food processor until fine. Cut thin strips of peel off the orange. Chop orange pulp and add peel and pulp to processor and chop again. Set aside.
2. Combine gelatins with boiling water. Add remaining ingredients and cranberry mixture. Mix well. Chill until set in large mold or 9- by 13-inch pan.

*Yield: 12 ¾-cup servings*

| Nutritive values per ¾-cup serving: | CAL | CHO (gm) | PRO (gm) | FAT (gm) |
|---|---|---|---|---|
| | 71 | 10 | 1 | 3 |

Food exchanges per ¾-cup serving:                    1 FRUIT, ½ FAT

# Cran-Apple Crisp

    2 medium tart apples, sliced (about 3 cups)
 1½ cups fresh cranberries
    ¼ cup unsweetened orange juice
    1 tablespoon grated orange zest
    ⅓ cup unbleached white flour
    ⅓ cup quick oats, uncooked
    ¼ cup Brown SugarTwin
    1 teaspoon ground cinnamon
    ¼ teaspoon ground nutmeg
    2 tablespoons corn or safflower oil

1. Preheat oven to 375°F.
2. In medium bowl, combine apples, cranberries, orange juice, and zest. Place in shallow 1½-quart baking dish.
3. In medium bowl, combine flour, oats, Brown Sugar-Twin, cinnamon, nutmeg, and oil until crumbly. Sprinkle over apple mixture. Bake 25 minutes or until apples are tender and topping is golden. Serve warm.

*Yield: 6 ¾-cup servings*

| Nutritive values per ¾-cup serving: | CAL | CHO (gm) | PRO (gm) | FAT (gm) |
|---|---|---|---|---|
| | 128 | 22 | 1 | 4 |

Food exchanges per ¾-cup serving:     ½ BREAD, 1½ FRUIT, 1 FAT

# Easy Sugarless Pumpkin Pie

      2  eggs, slightly beaten
      1  16-ounce can pureed pumpkin
     12  packets artificial sweetener (equal to ½ cup
         sugar)
      ½  teaspoon salt
      1  teaspoon ground cinnamon
      ½  teaspoon ground ginger
      ¼  teaspoon ground cloves
      1  teaspoon vanilla extract
      1  12-ounce can evaporated skim milk
      1  9-inch unbaked homemade pie crust (Lean
         Pie Crust; see index) or frozen pie shell

**1.** Preheat oven to 425°F.
**2.** Combine filling ingredients in order given.
**3.** Pour into pie shell.
**4.** Bake 15 minutes. Reduce temperature to 350°F and
   bake an additional 45 minutes or until knife inserted
   near center of pie comes out clean.

*Yield: 1 9-inch pie (8 servings)*

| Nutritive values per serving: | | CHO | PRO | FAT |
|---|---|---|---|---|
| | CAL | (gm) | (gm) | (gm) |
| | 176 | 29 | 6 | 4 |

Food exchanges per serving:     1½ BREAD, ½ MILK, 1 FAT

# Master List of Recipes

## APPETIZERS

Bean Dip, *page* 95
Devilish Eggs, *page* 99
Dip for Vegetables or Sort-
   of Sour Cream, *page* 94
Homemade Tortilla Chips,
   *page* 97

Meatball Snacks, *page* 98
Peanut Dip, *page* 96
Popcorn Treat, *page* 98
Sesame Nachos, *page* 97

## BEVERAGES

Banana Shake, *page* 15
Chocolate Shake, *page* 92
Grape Soda, *page* 92
Homemade Cocoa Mix,
   *page* 17
Orange-Pineapple Shake,
   *page* 16

Pineapple Shake, *page* 91
Spiced Tea, *page* 93
Strawberry Shake,
   *page* 16

## SOUPS

Corn Chowder, *page* 67
Egg Drop Soup, *page* 61
Greek Lemon Soup,
   *page* 73
Lentil Soup, *page* 71
Manhattan Clam Chowder,
   *page* 66
Matzo Ball Soup, *page* 64

Minestrone, *page* 62
Navy Bean Soup, *page* 63
Potato and Turnip Soup,
   *page* 72
Split Pea Soup, *page* 69
Vegetable-Beef Soup,
   *page* 68
Vegetable Soup, *page* 70

# BREADS AND CEREALS

Applesauce Muffins,
  page 44
Apple Spice Oatmeal,
  page 21
Baked Apple Pancake,
  page 31
Banana Bread, page 39
Blueberry Muffins,
  page 45
Bran Crêpes, page 35
Buttermilk Biscuits,
  page 38
Cinnamon Toast, page 29
French Toast, page 30
Gloria's Corn Bread,
  page 37
High-Protein Three-Grain
  Bread, page 40

Lemon Muffins, page 48
Multigrain Pancakes,
  page 32
Oat Bran Muffins,
  page 47
Oatmeal Bread, page 122
Orange Cottage Cheese
  Muffins, page 46
Popovers, page 221
Raisin Cheese Toast,
  page 28
Refrigerator Bran Muffins,
  page 42
Stovetop Granola, page 22
Whole Grain Irish Soda
  Bread, page 42
Zucchini Bread, page 124

# MAIN COURSES

## MEAT

### BEEF AND VEAL

Beef and Snow Peas,
  page 180
Beef and Tomato Stir-Fry,
  page 178
Gloria's Spaghetti Sauce
  with Meat, page 144
Homemade Sausage,
  page 23
Lasagne with Meat and
  Vegetables, page 136
Lean Pastichio, page 176
Oriental Flank Steak,
  page 179

Osso Buco, page 186
Pot Roast, page 181
Superb Oven Stew,
  page 184
Swiss Steak, page 183
Veal Chops with Raspberry
  Vinegar, page 188
Veal Scaloppine, page 185
Vegetable and Meat Loaf,
  page 182

## LAMB

Baked Lamb Chops,
*page* 191
Greek Lamb Chops,
*page* 189

Lovely Lamb Stew,
*page* 190

## PORK

Orange Pork Chops with
Rice, *page* 192

## POULTRY

BBQ Chicken, *page* 157
Brunswick Stew, *page* 162
Chicken Cacciatore,
*page* 153
Chicken Cordon Bleu,
*page* 161
Chicken Pizzaiola,
*page* 160
Chicken and Vegetable
Stir-Fry, *page* 152
Foiled Chicken, *page* 155
Lemon Chicken, *page* 151
Lemon Chicken with
Bulgur, *page* 154

Orange Chicken, *page* 156
Oven-Fried Chicken,
*page* 158
Peanut Butter Chicken,
*page* 159
Roast Stuffed Turkey,
*page* 164
Turkey Burgers, *page* 167
Turkey Chili, *page* 80
Turkey Loaf, *page* 163
Turkey Tetrazzini,
*page* 168

## FISH

Foiled Fish Fillets,
*page* 173
Oven Fish Fillets,
*page* 174
Oven "French-Fried"
Scallops, *page* 171

Salmon Croquettes,
*page* 174
Saucy Scallops, *page* 172
Seafood Stew, *page* 170

# PASTA SALADS, SANDWICHES, VEGETARIAN DISHES

Baked Macaroni and
Cheese, *page* 78
Cheese Blintzes, *page* 34
Chili Deluxe with
Vegetables, *page* 81

Chinese Chicken Salad,
*page* 148
Eggs Benedict, *page* 24
Fast Spaghetti Sauce with
Spaghetti Squash, *page* 146

Gloria's Spaghetti Sauce,
  Meatless, *page* 144
Linguine with Red Clam
  Sauce, *page* 135
Mini Pizzas, *page* 76
Open-Faced Tuna Melts,
  *page* 74
Pasta with Tuna and
  Tomato Sauce, *page* 139

Pita Pockets, *page* 75
Sloppy Joes, *page* 77
Spinach Manicotti,
  *page* 138
Taco Salad, *page* 150
Tamale Pie, *page* 142
Whole Wheat Pizza,
  *page* 140

# VEGETABLES
## STARCHY

Carrot–Acorn Squash,
  *page* 203
Oven-Fried Squash,
  *page* 206
Puffed Sweet Potatoes,
  *page* 201
Spaghetti Squash, *page* 147

Squash with Apples,
  *page* 205
Stuffed Yams, *page* 200
Sweet Potatoes and
  Bananas, *page* 202

## NONSTARCHY

Baked Spinach, *page* 213
Cauliflower or Broccoli
  Parmesan, *page* 207
Chinese Vegetables,
  *page* 219
Continental Green Beans,
  *page* 212
Fruit Spiced Carrots,
  *page* 211
Hash Brown Turnips,
  *page* 218
Mashed Turnips, *page* 217

Sautéed Cabbage,
  *page* 210
Sesame Broccoli, *page* 208
Skillet Vegetables,
  *page* 220
Stir-Fry Squash, *page* 214
Swiss Chard Sauté,
  *page* 216
Tart Red Cabbage,
  *page* 209
Zucchini Italiano,
  *page* 215

# SIDE DISHES AND SALADS

Apple Salad, *page* 105
Baked Beans, *page* 79
Bulgur Pilaf, *page* 196

Carrot and Raisin Salad,
  *page* 104
Coleslaw, *page* 84

Corn Pudding, *page* 204
Cranberry Mold, *page* 233
Cucumber Salad, *page* 212
German Potato Salad,
*page* 83
New Potato Salad,
*page* 82
Noodle Kugel, *page* 193
Oven "French Fries,"
*page* 197

Potato-Bean Patties,
*page* 198
Potato Kugel, *page* 199
Red Beans and Rice,
*page* 194
Rice and Vegetable
Casserole, *page* 195
Special Fruited Coleslaw,
*page* 85
Stuffing for Turkey, *page* 166

## SAUCES, DRESSINGS, AND CONDIMENTS

All-American Cranberry
Sauce, *page* 231
Applesauce, *page* 52
Blueberry Jam Spread,
*page* 50
Chocolate Sauce, *page* 230
Cranberry Relish,
*page* 232
Creamy Vinaigrette,
*page* 225
Fresh Blueberry Sauce,
*page* 51
Gravy from Meat
Drippings, *page* 227
Low-Calorie Mayonnaise,
*page* 226

Microwave Peach Jam,
*page* 50
Mock Hollandaise Sauce,
*page* 25
Mock Sour Cream, *page* 36
Mock Thousand Island
Dressing, *page* 224
Mustard Sauce, *page* 175
No-Calorie Dressing,
*page* 222
Strawberry Jam, *page* 49
Strawberry Sauce, *page* 36
Tangy Buttermilk
Dressing, *page* 223

## SWEET TREATS AND DESSERTS

Ambrosia, *page* 19
Apple Crunch, *page* 111
Applesauce Bran Squares,
*page* 118
Baked Custard, *page* 106
Berry Yogurt, *page* 18
Bread Pudding, *page* 26

Brennan's Rice Pudding,
*page* 107
Carrot Snack Cake,
*page* 119
Cherry Pie, *page* 113
Chocolate Chip Cookies,
*page* 109

Chocolate Delight,
   page 229
Cran-Apple Crisp,
   page 234
Easy Sugarless Pumpkin
   Pie, page 235
Fresh Peach Pie, page 116
Frozen Banana, page 101
Frozen Fruit Pops,
   page 102
Graham Cracker Crust,
   page 115
Lean Pie Crust, page 114
Lemon Snow Pudding,
   page 228
Oatmeal Cookies,
   page 112
Orange Sherbert,
   page 102

Peach Whip, page 100
Peach Yogurt, page 18
Peanut Butter Cookies,
   page 108
Pineapple Sherbert,
   page 103
Quick Banana Cream Pie,
   page 114
Spiced Baked Apples,
   page 20
Robin's Favorite: Sweet
   Potato Pie, page 27
Vanilla Cheesecake,
   page 120
Whole Grain Pastry Shell,
   page 117
"Wholesome" Brownies,
   page 110